Ancient Peoples and Places

BONES, BODIES, AND DISEASE

EVIDENCE OF DISEASE AND ABNORMALITY IN EARLY MAN

General Editor
DR. GLYN DANIEL

Ancient Peoples and Places

BONES, BODIES, AND DISEASE

EVIDENCE OF DISEASE AND ABNORMALITY IN EARLY MAN

Calvin Wells

88 PHOTOGRAPHS
33 LINE DRAWINGS
4 TABLES
3 GRAPHS
I HISTOGRAM

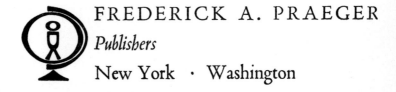

FREDERICK A. PRAEGER
Publishers
New York · Washington

THIS IS VOLUME THIRTY-SEVEN IN THE SERIES

Ancient Peoples and Places

GENERAL EDITOR: DR. GLYN DANIEL

BOOKS THAT MATTER

Published in the United States of America
in 1964 by Frederick A. Praeger, Inc.
Publishers, 111 Fourth Avenue
New York 3, N.Y.
Second printing, 1965
Library of Congress Catalog Card Number: 64-12018
© Calvin Wells 1964
Printed in Great Britain

To Freddie

CONTENTS

ILLUSTRATIONS

Foreword

To ACKNOWLEDGE THE HELP of all those to whom I have turned whilst writing this book is to recall in pleasant retrospect many friendly encounters and exchanges of correspondence. I should like to think that no oversight has led me to neglect with apparent ingratitude the kindness and courtesy that have been so often extended to me.

For help in obtaining illustrations, for permission to rummage in their museum collections, or for miscellaneous assistance I am much indebted to Mr Cyril Aldred, Dr Dietrich von Bothmer, Prof. J. D. Boyd, Dr D. R. Brothwell, the late Mr R. R. Clarke, Mr Warren R. Dawson, Miss Jessie Dobson, Dr A. J. Duggan, Prof. P. V. Glob, Mr Charles Green, Prof. Margherita Guarducci, Dr C. J. Hackett, Charles F. Hayes III, Mr R. A. Higgins, Dr A. Klasens, Dr. V. Møller-Christensen, Mr K. C. Murray, Mrs Walter Neurath, Dr K. P. Oakley, Miss Rosemary Powers, Dr L. W. Proger, Mr D. F. Renn, Dr Yusef Saad, Dr A. T. Sandison, Mr H. de S. Shortt, Dr Laurence Sickman, Mlle Claudine Sudre, Dr J. C. Trevor, Mr J. B. Ward Perkins and Prof. A. W. Woodruff. For unusual favours and for aid beyond the bounds of expectation I must give my warmest thanks to Dr G. H. S. Bushnell, Mr Adrian Digby, Mr W. B. Fagg, Miss K. Kemper, Dr G. P. Larwood and Mrs Tamara Talbot-Rice.

I am most grateful to Dr Glyn Daniel for having invited me to write this book and to Messrs Thames and Hudson, above all Mr Eric Peters, for having endured my waywardness in the process with tolerant equanimity and unstinted help.

I owe an altogether special debt of thanks to Mr Correlli Barnett who read the typescript and advised me with penetrating wisdom; to Prof. H. A. Harris who also read it and offered valuable suggestions; to Miss Susan Puddy for her scrupulous exactitude in drawing the figures; and to Mrs Joan Dudley who, as a labour of friendship, grappled with the preparation of the manuscript.

My debt to Freddie transcends all reckoning and all acquittance: to her I dedicate this book in love and gratitude.

C. W.

CHAPTER I

The Significance of Palaeopathology

In the dead behold the quick.
DOROTHY WELLESLEY

THE PATTERN OF DISEASE or injury that affects any group of people is never a matter of chance. It is invariably the expression of stresses and strains to which they were exposed, a response to everything in their environment and behaviour. It reflects their genetic inheritance (which is their internal environment), the climate in which they lived, the soil that gave them sustenance and the animals or plants that shared their homeland. It is influenced by their daily occupations, their habits of diet, their choice of dwelling and clothes, their social structure, even their folklore and mythology. This realization that 'Man is a whole with his environment', though at least as old as Galen, is still a neglected precept despite the fact that it underlies the study of disease, in ancient peoples no less than in the living. Many anthropological accounts of early skeletons still ignore the evidence of pathology whilst diligently mincing every detail of normal anatomy. Yet what is normal in a population tends to express, above all, its genetic constitution, the inborn racial characters that are least affected by environment. Disease and injury mirror more faithfully the haps and mishaps imposed by the vagaries of life and the struggle to survive. If we seek the genetic affinities of an individual or group, details of normal anatomy and physiology are usually our most rewarding study; for the more intimate knowledge of how people have responded to the aggression of their environment pathology is a surer guide.

This principle is familiar enough from diseases of modern times. Miner's elbow, painter's colic, stoker's cataract, caisson disease and chimney-sweep's cancer all result from specialized ways of earning a living. Tennis elbow and footballer's cartilage derive from recreational hazards; chauffeur's fracture of the thumb, due to cranking cars, was a brief comment on a mechanical invention and its disappearance marked the technical advance of automatic starters. Smoker's cough and alcoholic neuritis are the product of widespread social customs; detergent allergy of domestic preference. The frequency of fractures in the neck of the thigh bone closely parallels the increasing longevity of the population since they are especially likely to occur in old people. Frost-bite, sunstroke and endemic goitre are responses to extremes of climate or geological peculiarities; malaria, plague and yellow fever, which depend on animal vectors for their transmission, are related to the total biological balance of the region. Anxiety states reveal the tension under which many people lead their lives and religious mania stems from part of our mythology.

These instances could be multiplied a thousandfold both for the present and the past. The first anonymous victim of a palaeolithic arrowhead ushered in a new phase of human activity as surely as the first man to be killed (in 1879) by industrial electric shock.

This intricate relationship between a people's way of life and the diseases they endure is the chief reason for the study of palaeopathology. It will be implicit throughout this book that ancient episodes of morbidity should always be examined for what they can tell about life in ancient places and this will vary according to the type, and especially the amount, of evidence that is available. A single incontestable case of leprosy or tuberculosis proves that the disease existed in a certain place at a definite time which must be determined on archaeological evidence. A single fracture may tell nothing beyond the fact that some neolithic farmer, perhaps hazy with metheglin and lurching bed-ward through a moth-warm autumn dusk, snapped his shin bone in a drunken stumble. Many such fractures, as are found among the Anglo-Saxons, or their comparative infrequency as with the ancient Egyptians, must subtend from strong contrasts in the way these people lived.

We can explain some patterns of disease more easily than others. In early Peruvian sites many skulls have been dug up with small, round depressed fractures of the vault; more than a dozen of them may be present on a single skull. They are remarkably uniform in appearance and are at once intelligible in the light of the frequent archaeological discovery of sling stones among the weapons in the burial grounds. Sometimes no clue can be found to explain an osseous change: the cause of a dense inflammation of the long bones that is confined to Australian aboriginal skeletons remains a matter of speculation. It is probably due to some local infection by a strain of organisms no longer recoverable or to unknown factors of heredity or environment that determine a peculiar type of tissue response in the natives. Clinical experience of disease teaches that many pathological conditions are restricted to very narrow geographical limits and sometimes a brief chronological range as well. The 'sweating sickness', which was a clearly defined entity running a dramatic course with a high mortality, suddenly appeared in England at the end of the fifteenth century. It remained localized there or in nearby parts of Europe and after five or six major recurrences in the ensuing century vanished as mysteriously as it had come, never to appear again. We must also recognize that an exact diagnosis of disease from ancient remains is often impossible. A pathological bone recovered from a burial ground is always a fact divorced from its context. Every diseased specimen lying on the laboratory bench and requiring a diagnosis is inevitably the end result of an illness which may, perhaps, have lasted for months or even years. The complete understanding of that end result, that enigmatic bone, may only be possible if the complicated details of its preceding clinical history are available. In disease of the living all doctors rightly attach great importance to a meticulous investigation of the patient's history before they attempt to diagnose his complaint. It is precisely because this history is denied us in the realm of prehistoric illness that a profound clinical knowledge is needed to solve the problems that are met. It is most unwise for anthropologists who lack clinical training to venture into the infinitely subtle field of ancient disease. Nothing is easier or more tempting than to strain the evidence, and constant vigilance is needed; in palaeopathology the best opinions are usually tentative opinions. However, a book of this kind would be intolerable to read, were each diagnosis to be qualified with its due rigmarole of hesitation and alternatives; and apparent incaution and overconfidence, should they be found, will therefore be due to the avoidance of such minuteness for the sake of clarity.

Throughout the ages man is seen in health and hubris strutting the plateaux or savannahs with a fine show of bravura. Stricken with disease he can only creep to his lair like any other whimpering beast. As we gaze in wonder at the rugged strength of the Rhodesian Man, awed by the craggy buttresses of his browridges and the massive sweep of his muzzle, our imagination is slow to see the end of this strange creature; to see him, long accustomed to the pain of rotting teeth and dental abscesses, now maddened by the agony of acute mastoid infection, enfeebled by toxins from the mounting pressure of pus within the bone, pus which had already plunged into the tissues of his neck and even tracked into the cavity of his cranium, bemusing him with headache, throbbing vertiginously at every toss of the great skull; a crazed and pitiable object, panting with fever as his last hours drip slowly away, untended and unassuaged. We must not be too precise; that final scene is forever vanished and unknowable and we delude ourselves if we think that its exact details can be recovered.

Plate 1

We can only conjecture and infer. But some such picture must be close to what really happened and the aim of palaeopathology is always to reconstruct these episodes as accurately as possible and to assess, for the group no less than for the individual, the full significance of the diseases that are identified. In doing this we should also note that the interrelationship of culture and disease is a two-way process in which the health status of a population is often seen to have a profound effect on its cultural attainments and even its survival.

The ambiguity of skeletal evidence often makes it difficult to interpret. Even in the fairly straightforward example of the Rhodesian skull widely divergent judgements have been passed. It has been suggested that the hole in the left temporal bone that can be seen in Plate 1 is not due to a spontaneously discharging abscess but results from a deliberate attempt to drain it by some primitive surgical operation, or that it may be an arrow or spear wound, or that it was made by the bite of a leopard or other large carnivore, or even by the post-mortem burrowing of beetles. He is a rash man who is dogmatic about an ancient bone.

Another point arises from study of the Rhodesian skull. Although the finer details remain obscure we can reasonably assume that its extensive pathological changes ended by killing its owner. This is exceptional. In the great majority of skeletons no trace remains of the cause of death. The reason for this is that lethal diseases which attack only soft tissues are far more common than those affecting bone. When pneumonia, dysentery, cerebral haemorrhage, epidemic diseases, coronary thrombosis and countless other ailments kill they leave no skeletal evidence of their passing. Even when pathological bones are recovered from excavations the lesions they show are more often than not healed disease—old repaired fractures, subsided inflammation, ossified blood-clots—and throughout the study of palaeopathology only a small proportion of ancient morbidity, probably less than one per cent, can ever be recog-nized. This indicates how deficient our knowledge of pre-historic illness must always remain.

CHAPTER II

The Evidence Available

. . . compell'd
Even to the teeth and forehead of our faults
To give in evidence.

WILLIAM SHAKESPEARE

T HE EVIDENCES OF ANCIENT DISEASE are of two
kinds: primary and secondary. Primary evidence consists
of the actual survival of some part of what was once a living
body; the fractured teeth of a Krapina Neandertal and the club-
foot of Pharaoh Siptah are of this kind. At its best this evidence   *Fig. 1*
is unimpeachable; the injury or disease can be examined
minutely, it can be handled, photographed and X-rayed. If
the bones are well preserved a case of vertebral osteochondritis
from the English Bronze Age admits of no ambiguity and   Plate 2
provided that the archaeological date is beyond dispute it
establishes the occurrence of this disease at that epoch. But all
too often such evidence is treacherously uncertain. The specimen may be a bad one, eroded by acid soils or crusted with a
deposit which masks one disease whilst simulating another, an
undecipherable palimpsest. Even if the bone is well preserved
the pathological changes may be slight and allow only a tentative diagnosis, perhaps a choice of two or three conditions.
Yet even the most equivocal of primary evidence has about it a
quality of immediacy which is an apanage of its essential nature.

The secondary sources are the documents and artifacts which
describe disease or hint at its existence. The best of them are
direct, detailed and explicit. But although secondary evidence
is often superior to primary it inevitably lacks the silver cord
of kinship which, roving back into the twilit dawn of antiquity,
binds us to the surviving corporal relics, however tattered or

23

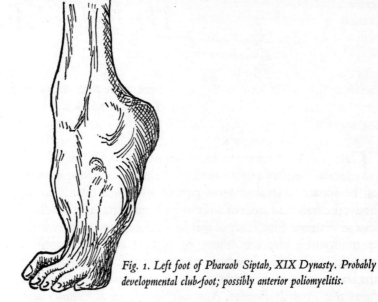

Fig. 1. Left foot of Pharaoh Siptah, XIX Dynasty. Probably developmental club-foot; possibly anterior poliomyelitis.

ill-treated by man, nature and time, of long-vanished men and women.

Of the primary sources the most important are bones, if for no other reason than that they far transcend in abundance any other kind of evidence. Yet until recently they were the ill-favoured disjecta of the excavator's haul and even today . . . but perhaps it is better not to write the sorry tale! Chance plays a great part in the survival of skeletal material. In many acid gravels and river terraces the effect of soil erosion is to destroy the bones in a few centuries or even decades. Where the percolation and infusion of stalagmitic minerals take place the remains may be preserved indefinitely as, for example, the Fontéchevade pre-Neandertals. In other sites, such as the Niah caves in Sarawak, the conditions of fossilization do not exist. Bone and all other perishables wither away and without benefit of geology return to the dust from which they briefly arose. But human remains have been found in an infinite variety of resting-places; lacustrine sediments, volcanic tufas, the peat bogs of Tollund and the caves of Chou Kou Tien have all given up their dead in varying states of preservation. Among the factors affecting the condition of bones are exposure to alternating extremes of heat and cold, alternate flooding and drying, attack by burrowing animals; insect, fungal or bacterial action, and penetration by the roots of plants. When the combined effect of these agents of destruction is added to the negligence of man himself it is astonishing that so much skeletal material has drifted to the relatively safe haven of competently organized museums. Independently of the soil the condition of the bones themselves affects their survival. Some diseases, such as osteomyelitis in which abscesses are present in the marrow cavity, may hasten their decay. Other lesions, for example 'ivory' tumours of the skull, are unusually resistant.

Next to bones the most important sources of primary material are mummies. These are of two main types, deliberately contrived specimens and those which have been produced by accidental causes like natural desiccation in hot sandy deserts. The master embalmers of the ancient world were, of course, the Egyptians. After four millennia of mummification vast numbers existed at the fall of the Coptic empire but many of them have been ravished by grave robbers seeking gold for wealth or mummia for lust. Even so, plenty have survived and for the student of disease they have the supreme advantage that soft tissues as well as bones are recovered. The details varied slightly with the dynasty but the basic method of Egyptian embalming was to surround the body with a packing of natron (sodium carbonate) and to use resin and spices to complete the process. At its best mummification preserves the body with exemplary perfection but the embalmers were often negligent, so sluttish work or outright faking of the packs is commonplace. Viscera were often damaged during their removal to the four Canopic jars, bones were misplaced, and animal remains or even pieces of wood were sometimes used to pad out the mummy. Within a shell of lacquered cartonnage, jewel-bright with painted scenes of Thoth and Horus, a shambles of deceit may repose.

Plate 3

Not all mummification is Egyptian. The custom has been widely scattered throughout the world. Smoke-drying for as much as six or eight weeks on end is recorded for the Ao and the Naga of Assam. In the same region the Khasi have been described as embalming the corpse in honey to preserve it for cremation at a later date. This expedient of temporary preserva-tion is an interesting and ancient one. The migratory pattern of life among the Scythians several centuries before the Christian era required that burial rites should take place only twice a year: embalming was a necessary response to this demand. The use of honey for mummification is mentioned in the ancient Indian books of the *Vishnu Purana* together with curds, ghee, musk, saffron, camphor and sandal, and madder-dyed cere-ments of silk and flowered muslin.

In Timor and among the Toradja of Celebes exposure in an open coffin hoisted into the branches of a tree has been recorded and similar methods have been practised by the Philippine Igorot, in New Guinea, Melanesian, Polynesian and numerous other groups. In North America mummies have been found from as far apart as Alaska, Virginia, Montana and Mexico, as well as many intervening sites. In the south-eastern area the skin was slit down the back and flensed from the eviscerated body, it was oiled to prevent it from shrinking, the muscles were stripped from the bones which were then dried on hurdles and finally the remains were replaced in the skin. With this method the testimony of soft tissues is pared almost to vanishing point.

The Aleutian Islands have yielded many carcases which have been stuffed with moss and grasses after evisceration but the

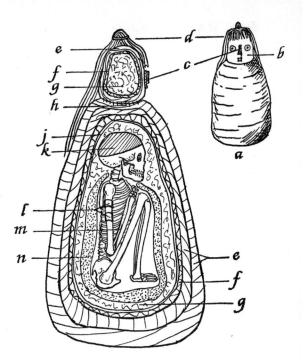

Fig. 2. A schematic representation of a Peruvian mummy pack. Precolumbian, c. A.D. 1000. a. external appearance of a mummy pack; b. painted face; c. wooden nose; d. imitation hair of agave fibre; e. coloured cotton swaddlings; f. marsh-reed netting; g. cotton floss packing; h. stitches joining the head to the body; j. woven cotton envelope; k. turban; l. silver bracelets; m. mummy in a contracted posture; n. cushma or tunic.

richest source in the New World, and second only to Egypt, has been Peru. Great numbers of mummies have been re-covered and many pathological specimens occur as well as a high proportion of neonatal and infant packs. Peruvian mummies are often found sitting up, with knees trussed against their chest, like gigantic shrivelled cicadas swathed in cocoons of exquisite fabrics. A somewhat special form of mummifica-tion is the tsantsa or shrunken head, well known from the Jívaro people of Ecuador. These duodecimo versions of the noble savage are somewhat illusory: it is only the skin and underlying soft tissues that are treated. The bones are removed through an occipital incision before the process of shrinking is begun. Skin diseases may sometimes be found in these heads but in general they provide slender material for the palaeo-pathologist.

Fig. 2

Plate 4

Of much greater use are those remains which have been recovered from peat bogs, mostly in Denmark and Germany. These bog finds vary greatly in their state of preservation; the best of them are more perfect than the finest Egyptian mummies. In the strangled Tollund man even the porridge which was his last meal still lay grumous and half-digested in his belly; the Windeby girl from Schleswig had a brain so well preserved that it could be sectioned for microscopic study; the young woman from Peiting in Bavaria survived death unputrefied and the dissection of her heart has been accomplished with as much precision as in a modern anatomical preparation. Yet these people lived two thousand years ago and could have heard the trumpets of Vercingetorix or looked with hate-darkened eyes upon the bloody carnage of the rout of Varus. Unfortunately bog finds as flawless as these are rarities. The unblemished perfection of the woman from Peiting depends on inhibition of the proteolytic enzymes that are normally produced and that lead to spontaneous mouldering of the tissues by auto-digestion. The inhibiting substance appears to be cholesterol which attained a concentration of 30 per cent in the brain of this specimen—about ten times its usual value.

Other soft tissue relics of the ancient dead are also rare and usually too frayed by the passage of time to be revealing of disease. A few chance finds of skin and hair survive. In 1959 a small fragment of brain was found inside the skull of a Romano-British burial from Droitwich. Its preservation was due to adipocere, a waxy substance which under rare conditions of sterility or chemical peculiarity forms a conserving pellicle around the tissues. Another example, probably of Bronze Age date, had been found in a British bog at Scaleby Moss, Cumberland, as long ago as 1843 but a much bigger discovery of this kind was a series of a hundred and twenty bodies from a glacial clay cemetery in the end moraine of the old Glinth glacier in Switzerland. This evidently furnished ideal conditions for the production of adipocere although the chemical details of the process are still not entirely understood.

One other form of almost perfect preservation must be mentioned: freezing. A very few sporadic cases have been reported from high Andean and Arctic sites but the only place where these frozen bodies have been found as a typical feature of the area is the Altai region of Central Asia round Başadar and Pazirik. Here, owing to a unique conjunction of climate, terrain and burial ritual, the remains of 'kindred Scythians' have lain in icy splendour, frost spangled and without decay, for over two millennia.

The last form of primary evidence to be considered is cremation. There is little doubt that these splintered cinders of the past are its Cinderellas, too. Brittle and broken, they have been jettisoned from their urns by generations of contemptuous archaeologists. It is true that the startling discovery, the pistol-shot effect, is seldom found among these harvests of the pyre, yet patience and tenacity can coax even these unlovely fragments to surrender new evidence of ancient ways and woes. There is an abundance of cremated material and pathological conditions such as dental caries, fractures and arthritis can be identified in it.

The principal secondary evidence of disease in antiquity comes from the works of early medical writers and historians. Included here are the Ebers and the Edwin Smith papyri, the case books of Hippocrates, the magnificent 'Essay on Typhoid' by Chang Chung-ching and countless other texts. As literary evidence this material will be accorded only brief and incidental consideration in this book, the avowed purpose of which is to forsake the well-trodden road of textual sources in order to explore the lesser-known byways of skeletal remains. Non-literary material will find a place, however, and this ranges from palaeolithic cave paintings to relatively modern statues   Plate 5
in preliterate societies. This discrimination is arbitrary and

artificial. It is dictated by the design and compass of the volume, and the most complete understanding of the history of disease can only be attained by an approach which mingles the evidence from all possible sources. But it is important not to overrate the value of the early manuscripts and lest it should seem that they are dismissed here in too cavalier a fashion it is worth emphasizing that under a guise of adroit lucidity they often turn out to be monsters of ambiguity, little better than inkblot tests which can mean all things to all men. This is clearly seen in the account of the Antonine Pestilence which swept the empire and immobilized the Roman army after the Parthian war of the mid second century A.D. Historians persist in describing this visitation as 'typical bubonic plague' which is about the one disease we can be sure it was not. Galen, who saw and treated many cases, described it in terms which sound somewhat like smallpox. But his account is far too confused to clinch the diagnosis. So too with the epidemic that devastated Athens in the fifth century B.C. Thucydides has described it in deathless prose which comes ringing down the centuries like a knell from the stricken city. Yet, lynxeyed for detail though he was, the overall picture is gossamer vague and according to the taste of modern commentators it has been diagnosed as scarlet fever, smallpox, influenza, typhoid, typhus, cerebrospinal meningitis and ergotism.

We may now briefly discuss a few points arising from the various nonliterary art forms on which we shall draw. The fact that we are dealing with some sort of representational product at once poses a problem as to its relationship with the object it depicts. How reliable is a statue or a painting as a document for diagnosing disease? How much is it merely an artistic convention? The problem will be met in discussing the Amarna style of sculpture and the possibility of artificial head moulding in ancient Egypt. There can be no universal solution. It is inherent in the arts that some forms, primitive no less

*Fig. 3. Rock painting from Jabbaren, Central Sahara. Highly conven-
tionalized style. Uncertain date.*

than modern, are more naturalistic than others. Each must be
judged on its merits; each must be assessed with sympathy and
intuition against what is known of the prevailing artistic conventions of the period and place. The filiform style of the
Jabbaren frescoes in mid-Sahara could only lead to a diagnosis
of some wasting disease associated, perhaps, with an endocrine
growth disorder, but it is clear that in reality these slender,
emaciated figures are as much a convention as the chubby
putti of the Italian Baroque.

    The oldest evidence of this type is found in palaeolithic
paintings, those remote masterpieces without a past which yet
foreshadow generations of the sublimest conceptions of the
human mind. Unfortunately the information they give about

Fig. 3

disease is scanty, not because the ancient hunters were remarkably healthy but because they seldom seem to have felt any
incentive to portray the human figure. Statues of a similarly
early date are also rare and it is not until the full dawning of
civilization in the Nile valley and the Middle East that these
sources of information become plentiful, together with bas-
reliefs which may be thought of as filling to some extent a half-
way position between engravings on antler or rock and sculpture in the round. Egyptian art sometimes depicts abnormalities
and disease but much of the information given—the frequent
occurrence of blindness for example—can equally well be
inferred from hieroglyphic texts in the papyri or cuneiform
records on clay tablets.

Plate 6

In non-literate societies these secondary sources of evidence
are a valuable addition to the information available from skeletal
remains, the more so because they commonly show abnormalities which do not affect bones and because whenever a pathological condition is portrayed in art it is apt to dominate the
artist and to break through, with naturalistic vigour, any
conventional style that may be the fashion of the time. This is
well seen in a charming bronze figure of an achondroplasic
dwarf from Benin, Nigeria.

Plate 7

In the field of painting some of the earliest examples are
amongst the most perplexing. Human hands of palaeolithic
workmanship are found on the walls of a dozen or more caves
in France and Spain. They are often 'negative' imprints, that
is the hand was placed against the wall and the pigment applied
round it. Nearly always these are left hands and this obviously
suggests that the average Aurignacian artist was right-handed.
In one cave, that of Gargas (Haute-Garonne), many of these
hands are found which have been mutilated by the loss of some
of the fingers. Almost all possible combinations occur including partial or total loss of the thumb. From modern practices
in many different tribes it has been assumed that these Gargas

Fig. 4

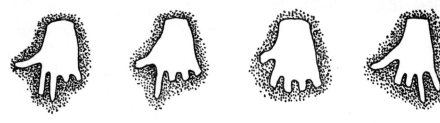

Fig. 4. Palaeolithic imprints of mutilated hands.

paintings represent a ritual or cult the purpose of which can now be only a matter of guesswork. But the loss of a thumb gravely incapacitates the victim and it seems hardly possible to find ethnological parallels for hand mutilation of such severity. This suggests that the Gargas imprints may be the result not of ritual but of disease. Almost all seem to be the hands of children or young women and this at once excludes the ordinary senile gangrene of arteriosclerosis. Their absence from Spanish caves might suggest that frost-bite was the cause because Spain was somewhat warmed by the Gulf Stream which, with the English Channel still unformed, could do little to ameliorate the cold of central France. The objection to this theory is that even in nearby French caves with an identical harsh climate these amputated fingers are not found. It seems possible, therefore, that these pollarded stumps were peculiar to the people of Gargas, that it was a hereditary affection and one which could attack young people. Diabetes, though possible, is on balance unlikely but Raynaud's disease, a form of spasm of the peripheral blood vessels that was later to be described by several classical authors, seems most admirably to fit the situation as far as it can be interpreted. A few other possibilities also need to be considered. One of these is leprosy but the absence of mutilations from other caves in the area would raise far-reaching problems of segregation. In palaeopathology, as in other sciences, imaginative insight is laudable enough: it must stop well short of delirium, however, and far stronger evidence will be needed

33

before Gargas can confidently be put forward as the world's first leper colony.

The ambiguity of much palaeolithic art is also shown in the well-known figure of a 'pregnant woman' from Laugerie Basse. Sigerist, usually a most cautious writer, even refers to her as 'a woman in childbirth'. There is no shred of evidence to support this judgement and though she may indeed be expecting a happy event it is idle to pretend that she could not equally well be suffering from an ovarian cyst. It is not until much later that painting gives relatively clear evidence of disease. Often this falls within the historic period and the graphic representations supplement literary evidence, as in the numerous scenes of blindness from ancient Egypt. Many of the sufferers are young people and this makes it possible to exclude glaucoma as a likely cause. Much of this blindness was probably due to cataract from traumatic ulcers caused by grit but in some cases it seems possible to recognize trachoma, a highly infectious condition that is still common in Egypt, and one which cannot be deduced with any confidence from the medical papyri.

Although painters are trained to observe and to depict, it is unsafe to rely on their testimony even late in the historical period. In the Chiesa degli Angeli at Lugano there is a Renaissance painting of St Roch, the patron saint of those smitten with the plague. A bubo is an enlarged, infected lymph gland and does not occur in other tissues, but in this painting the artist has shown St Roch pointing to a large bubo on his thigh in a position where no glands are found.

Plate 8

Amongst the numerous types of sculpture one with a wide distribution is the mask; even more important is the pot. Both provide many representations of diseases but the early Peruvian cups and water jugs of the Mochica and Chimú periods yield a crop of pathological portraiture which can scarcely be equalled in any other region. Great caution is needed when

inferring disease from pottery. These objects are realistic works
of art but they are utensils as well and their form may be coerced
by their function. Two excellent examples of pes planus—flat
foot—are seen in a neolithic tripartite jar from Hluboke
Masuvky and in a Lusatian culture clay model, probably the
pedestal of a jug, from Nasedlovice u Kyjova, Czechoslovakia.
In each case it would be reckless to diagnose an orthopaedic
defect from what is nothing more than a potter's device to
impart stability to his vessel.

Many other objects permit a fleeting glimpse of the ailments
of ancient peoples. Coins are a minor source: Vespasian is
unmistakably toothless in his old age and the portrait money of
Maximianus Herculius suggests that he had a broken nose. Plate 10
Netsuke and ex-votos are even more rewarding; platters, pipe-
bowls, cylinder seals, and mosaics augment the list. Even
fabrics may have a tale to tell: Turold's groom who stands in Plate 9
broidered immortality in the Bayeux tapestry is not the only
dwarf fretted in this medium. Oblique hints turn up in many
unexpected places. At Kahun in Egypt, a hand-high biconical
pot has been found which contained ozokerite (ceresin), a
natural paraffin wax that in the Old World occurs only at
Boryslaw in the Carpathians and at Tscheleken near Baku on
the Caspian. The discovery of this precious unguent in a
Middle Kingdom context cannot positively identify any
disease but it is very likely that it was used to allay the itching
of an eczema or to coax off the sequin scales of psoriasis.
Finally, there is the evidence of surgical instruments. At
Obermenzing in Bavaria and Kiskoszeg, Hungary, doctors'
graves of La Tène Iron Age date have been found. They
contained snares, retractors and amputation saws which can
have no meaning in the absence of injury or disease to give
occasion for their use. Apart from this confirmation of early
written accounts of amputations a Roman artificial leg, in
bronze over a wooden core, has also survived.

CHAPTER III

Types of Abnormalities

Terrible, strange, sublime and beauteous shapes.

P. B. SHELLEY

THE CATALOGUE of the ailments and abnormalities known to affect man is a long one. It includes thousands of morbid processes which together present a bewildering array of symptoms. To reduce this chaotic rabble of pathology to an orderly scheme of disease some form of classification must be devised. One of the best is to group these various conditions in terms of the anatomy and physiology of the body. This is systemic classification and leads to a consideration of diseases of the skin, diseases of bone, and cardiovascular, ophthalmic or neurological lesions. A second method is to group diseases according to their cause: congenital abnormalities, infection, allergy and other basic principles. Both methods are useful; neither is without its drawbacks. If, for instance, the pathology of the osseous system is under review it is easy enough to deal with Paget's disease which is, in effect, limited to bones; but tuberculosis, though commonly attacking the skeleton, occurs also in lungs, glands, skin, tendons and elsewhere. In other words, the conditions which attack any anatomical division of the body are likely to transgress the frontiers that this classification imposes. In the same way when illness is considered from the viewpoint of its aetiology a similar inadequacy is found. Various infections may give rise to swellings and deformities in bone: so also can deficiency diseases, malignant growths and certain degenerative changes of unknown origin.

The fact that no classification of disease is faultless does not matter as long as we are aware of the limitations of each and are ready to adapt our approach to the problem that confronts us. In everyday life, as it happens, we tend to think in terms of symptoms rather than diseases. Toothache is not a disease *sui generis*; it is a symptom which may result from dental caries, fracture, apical abscess, neuritis and many other conditions; cough can be due to mechanical or chemical irritation, infection, heart disease, cancer or emotional upsets. There is, too, the difficulty that the genesis of many diseases is unknown. Nevertheless it is on the basis of their underlying cause that we shall group them in this book. The classification will be: congenital abnormalities, injury, infection, degenerative conditions, growths, deficiency diseases, metabolic and endocrine disorders and conditions of unknown origin. Even this makes logic and strict conformity bow to convenience because some metabolic diseases—alkaptonuria is one—are in fact congenital. It is convenient also to abandon this aetiological classification for a regional one when discussing teeth; whilst some well-defined groups of disease, such as the allergies, will pass unnoticed because it is doubtful whether any real proof of their existence can be found in ancient skeletal material. This does not mean that they can be excluded. If hay fever and lobster urticaria are unlikely ever to be identified in a prehistoric context there is evidence of emphysema in an Egyptian mummy. This condition which is an over-stretching of the lung with a breakdown of its elastic tissue could be the result of allergic asthma, although it must be admitted that other causes are more likely.

CONGENITAL DISEASE

As thou knowest not what is the way of the spirit, nor how the bones do grow in the womb. . . .

ECCLESIASTES

There are two kinds of congenital abnormality or disease: those due to an inherited genetic deviation, and those due to

Plate 11

Fig. 5

some adverse factor affecting the foetus during its period of intra-uterine growth. Albinism, Huntingdon's chorea and colour blindness fall into the first group; in the second are congenital syphilis, deafness due to maternal rubella, hare-lip or deformities from the effect of a drug such as thalidomide. It is often impossible to know which of these two forms is responsible for an abnormality and here there is no need to discriminate minutely. We should note, however, that some of the genetic variants can hardly be regarded as abnormal and are certainly not diseases. The survival into adult life of a metopic suture, which divides the frontal bone of infants into two halves, is probably genetically determined. It is abnormal only in being a 'minority condition' that occurs with frequencies ranging from less than 1 per cent (Ainu) to twelve per cent (Germans). It must be very nearly neutral as far as survival value is concerned.

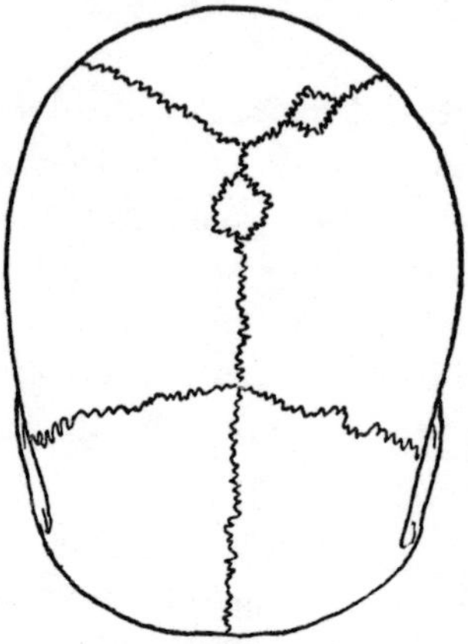

Fig. 5. Anomalous cranium showing a suture dividing the frontal bone into two halves and intersutural bones to the rear of the skull.

Fig. 6

Many anatomical aberrations are of this kind even though some, such as the feline type of epicondylar process on the humerus, are much more rare. On the other hand microcephaly, which stunts the growth of the skull and brain to result in idiocy, can also be genetic in origin but is so severely pathological that survival is only possible, if at all, under the mantle of modern welfare states.

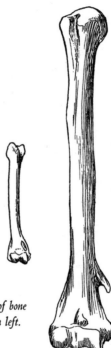

Fig. 6. Humerus with a congenital and anomalous process of bone near the lower end. Normal cat's humerus for comparison on left.

If a rare hereditary abnormality is found unusually often in a burial ground we should probably assume a blood relationship between the persons who show it. In the Early Christian vaults of Biga and Hesa, Nubia, several uncommon anomalies were repeatedly encountered and left little doubt that the people buried there were either members of one family or a closely inbred community. The gorilla type of breast bone and a rare form of shoulder blade were among the features that permitted this

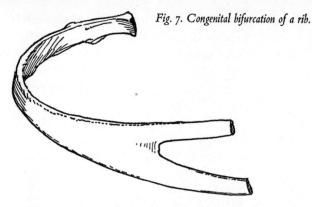

Fig. 7. Congenital bifurcation of a rib.

Fig. 7

Fig. 5

Plate 12

Fig. 8

inference. In an Anglo-Saxon group from Beckford, Gloucestershire, the presence of several individuals with bifid ribs suggested close kinship amongst them. Extra 'wormian' bones between the sutures of the skull and suppression of one or more teeth have a similar significance. Many of these conditions vary greatly in incidence. Congenital dislocation of the hip appears occasionally in cemeteries from most parts of the world but it attains exceptional frequencies, up to ten per cent, in Apache, Salteaux and some other Amerindian groups. The well-known Egyptian bas-relief of the Queen of Punt is almost certainly an example of this disease and a young woman twisted by its deformity is modelled in a Hellenistic bronze statuette in the J. Klejman collection, New York.

In a few conditions we cannot always decide whether they are truly congenital or not. One of the mummies in the famous 'Tomb of the Two Brothers' has a club-foot that may be prenatal in origin but could also be due to faulty development in early childhood, perhaps even the result of injury. Some people consider that the many Upper Palaeolithic female figurines with prominent 'steatopygous' buttocks are meant to portray a pathological fatness of a congenital type; but these Aurignacian Venuses closely resemble the modern Bushman and their gluteal adiposity, though frequently emphasized for symbolic reasons, should be regarded as a racial character that is in no way abnormal or diseased. One of the commonest and least harmful of deviations is polydactyly, which usually appears as a small supernumerary finger or toe. It is not a condition that is recognized skeletally. Even though it may have occurred quite often in ancient populations the tiny sliver of bone within the extra digit would either be lost through soil action or pass unnoticed in the excavation. But we may guess that it did occur: near Brasstown, Clay County, North Carolina, and in Scott County, Illinois, early petroglyphs have been

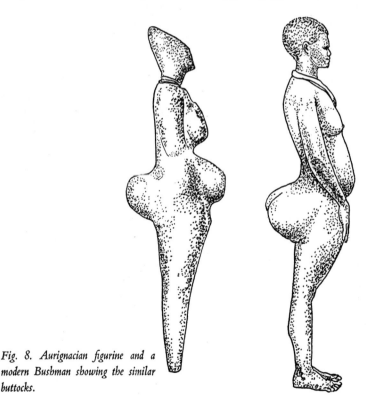

Fig. 8. Aurignacian figurine and a modern Bushman showing the similar buttocks.

found that show six-toed human feet. They are about sixteen inches long, clearly carved, and probably reflect a freak that the artist had known in real life.

One of the most impressive of congenital abnormalities is achondroplasia. In this disease the long bones of the limbs fail to grow, whilst most of the trunk bones are unaffected. The victim develops into a dwarf with diminutive arms and legs on an approximately normal torso. These are the dwarfs who often perform as circus acrobats. Their striking appearance, together with a natural agility of body and of temperament, never fails to attract attention. They seem to have been common in ancient Egypt where an achondroplasic skeleton was found at a predynastic Badarian site and another kept company with his royal master King Zer (I Dynasty) in his tomb at Abydos. Two more of these manikins lay in the sepulchre of Aba (2400 B.C.) and yet another pair in a V Dynasty tomb at Deshasheh. This indicates how common they were; the inter-est they provoked is proved by their frequent representation in bas-reliefs and statues. They seem to look after animals or to make and care for jewellery. The statue of Seneb is a perfect portrait of one of these dwarfs in which his grotesque figure is brilliantly contrasted with the comeliness of his wife and children. The gnarled and misshapen proportions of the Egyptian god Bes are said to mimic achondroplasia but this attribution is suspect. Nowhere else are these dwarfs so con-spicuous until we meet them again in European paintings from the Renaissance onward but their quaint appeal has won them fitful representation in the art of many different cultures and it is evident that this disease is an old one and widely spread.

Plate 13

Plates 7, 14

Some of the worst congenital abnormalities are those that produce imbeciles by malformations of the skull. Microcephaly has already been mentioned. Surviving examples of it from antiquity are too few to establish any pattern of incidence but it has been found at the neolithic site of Windmill Hill, Wiltshire, in a medieval mound at Donnybrooke, Eire, in a Darnley Island mummy and in ancient Patagonians. Its artistic portrayal appears in Hellenistic figurines and also in China where the divinity Lao-Tsay-Ho seems to be conceived as a microcephalic. Mental backwardness cannot be accurately gauged from the size of the head and in the case of an exceed-ingly small cranium from Chilca, Peru, there may have been no deficiency at all. Its volume (490 c.c.) would suit a gorilla and almost a chimpanzee. It is only about a third of the human average and it appears to be the skull of a normal midget rather than a pathological dwarf or imbecile. Hydrocephaly, which may result from post-natal as well as ante-natal causes, produces enlargement of the head. When severe it always damages the brain but minor degrees may leave no taint on intellectual ability. It is seldom recovered from ancient grave-yards, no doubt because most cases perish in early childhood, but at Norton, Yorkshire, a young man of Romano-British date was found who had an enormously dilated skull with a capacity of 2600 c.c.—two pints more than the average. Even this huge head falls well short of an Egyptian specimen of the same date that had a volume in excess of 2900 c.c. and in which a one-sided (hemiplegic) atrophy of the limb bones betrayed the extensive cerebral injury that went with it. Plate 15

Chromosomes are the structures on which genes are located. They are present in the nuclei of all cells, where they vary slightly in shape and size. Number twenty-one of the human series is nearly the smallest but if an extra one of these gets into the tissues as a developmental error the individual will be a mongol. Idiots of this kind have occasionally been identified in early burials. They, too, often die as children but at least one Andean lived long enough to bewitch the inquisitive eye and cunning fingers of some ancient potter. Another chromo-some mishap can produce hermaphrodites. The XVIII Plate 17

Dynasty Egyptian queen Hatshepsut, daughter of Thotmes I and his sister Aahmes, is often graven in murals of the period as a strongly masculine character. Despite ritual and political temptation to portray her in this way it is possible that this is a partial representation of a real intersex state, a condition that is by no means rare. Anencephaly, a monstrosity in which the child is born with total absence of the upper brain and the top of its head, has not yet been reported from antiquity apart from one case of an Egyptian mummified monkey.

Plate 16

Not all congenital malformations of the skull impair the intellect. Scaphocephaly, named from its likeness to the upturned keel of a felucca, is an unusual narrowing of the cranial vault due to premature fusion of the sagittal suture. It appears as an oddity in many ancient cemeteries and can hardly be described as pathological; it is one of several deformities produced by anomalous sutural behaviour and its recent discovery in a skull of dubious identity has helped to prove that this cranium belonged to the eighteenth-century philosopher Emanuel Swedenborg. Another minor trait, strongly linked to hereditary factors, is baldness. Rameses IV is one of a great many mummies showing advanced hair loss. The recognition of congenital disease is seldom possible apart from the direct anatomical evidence of bones or mummy tissue. Inborn physiological errors such as colour blindness and haemophilia remain irrecoverable. But from the radiographic examination of a precolumbian Mound Builder at Ozark Bluff, Arkansas, it seems almost certain that he suffered from sickle-cell anaemia, a serious blood dyscrasia that is especially common today in negroes. Whether the modern interest in blood grouping early mummies and skeletal remains, of which Madeleine Glemser has been the pioneer in this country, will ever extend to the identification of abnormal haemoglobins and such diseases as pernicious anaemia or chlorosis cannot at present be known without further research.

INJURY

When their bones are picked clean and the clean bones gone,
They shall have stars at elbow and foot.

DYLAN THOMAS

Life without injury can hardly be imagined. All vertebrates are ready victims of accidental fractures or deliberate wounding by tooth and claw. Insects and molluscs enjoy no better immunity. Foraminifera, diatoms and desmids may have their crisp exo-skeletons broken by direct violence and though a virus cannot be attacked with bow and arrow it is, no less than Eliot's hippopotamus, 'susceptible to nervous shock' from such physical processes as desiccation, ultra-violet radiation, rise of temperature or chemical change in the environment. Probably factors of this kind have existed as long as life itself and whilst the fossil record is silent on the pathology of pre-Cambrian viruses an abundance of fractured bones survives from the Permian, Cretaceous and later epochs where it is found that the long slender tails of plesiosaurs and similar creatures were peculiarly vulnerable to injury. It accords well with man's propensity for viciousness that his very first entrance upon the stage of human history resounds with the thunder of violence.

Skulls of Australopithecines—the South African proto-humans or 'man-apes'—have been found showing a distinctive form of fracture which consists of two depressions close together on the dome of the head. Antelope humeri have also been recovered in association with these skulls and the large articular condyles of these limb bones fit neatly into the double-valleyed depressions in the cranial fragments. There is no doubt that the heavy ungulate humeri were admirably suited for use as clubs and that a million years ago the precursors of sapient man were already nimble at battering their fellows in a way that is still only too familiar in an age of teddy-boys and apartheid.

The genus Pithecanthropus has been divided into several species including *P. erectus*, the Java ape-man and *P. sinensis*, the Pekin man (previously referred to as *Sinanthropus pekin-ensis*). More than a dozen individuals of the Java group are known and there is evidence that several of them met a violent end at the hands of their fellows, though it has also been sug-gested that like the Pompeians of A.D. 79 they were the victims of a volcanic eruption. These people date from perhaps half a million years ago. At a late palaeolithic site not far away on the Solo River another community has been found which con-sists of eleven skull caps roughly intermediate in form between their early Pithecanthropus neighbours and the Neandertals. Four of these eleven individuals had fatal head wounds. The Pekin group, which must have been nearly contemporary with Pithecanthropus, was found in a cave at Chou Kou Tien. Before the specimens were lost during the Second World War this material consisted of about forty individuals. Weiden-reich who examined it in great detail has said that every one of them died a violent death and was dismembered. In many of them heavy cudgel blows on the skull produced fissured depres-sions; in others some sort of axe or knife inflicted long deep furrows. At least one frontal bone had an old healed wound of this type. Above the site where these people were found is another cave which harboured the remains of an upper palaeo-lithic family of seven persons. Of these the 'Old Man' has a depressed fracture of his left temporal bone, an adult woman has a spear-like wound of her left parietal, two other skulls are fractured, one of which shows injuries caused both by clubs and a more pointed weapon. Three of this family were children, one new-born, and there can be little doubt that some enemy killed them all. What passions seethed round this bloody cave or what motive guided the hands which slaugh-tered here can never be known but such is the fashioning of human nature that it is easy to imagine that Clytemnestra dripping with the blood of Agamemnon would have felt some strange kinship with the scene enacted on this spot. At the Chinese eneolithic site of Sha Kuo T'un forty-five bodies seem to have been the victims of a ritual holocaust. At the mesolithic site of Ofnet in Bavaria thirty-three skulls, mostly of women and children, have been excavated. They were in two groups, packed tightly together like eggs in a nest. All had been hacked from their bodies and most of the cranial roofs had been bashed with some kind of lentiform weapon, prob-ably a hafted stone mallet.

Two points of immediate interest may be noted here apart from this impressive evidence of man's primeval pugnacity. The first is that even at this early period of human prehistory an examination of the skeletal injuries can give a clue to the type of weapon used however unspecialized it may have been. The second is that in all these instances the cause of death is recognizable. This is quite unusual and is almost entirely restricted to occasions when evidence of violence can be found. The vast majority of skeletons, even when showing gross pathological changes—which most do not—seldom reveal what the person died from. In a very small proportion of all speci-mens signs of advanced tuberculosis or some other infection, or the rare case of malignancy, may permit the cause of death to be inferred with fair probability.

In the examples from palaeolithic times which have just been mentioned the injuries were all caused by violent blows. With the advent of mesolithic cultures and increasingly throughout neolithic times flighted death from arrow-shot is met. An early example of this comes from the mesolithic cemetery of Téviec in Brittany. Here a body was found with a Tardenoisian triangle embedded in the sixth thoracic vertebra. From neolithic sites many dozens of skeletons have been recovered with flint arrowheads still in the bones and few parts of the body escaped. In the spine it is the lumbar region which is most commonly wounded, as for example in specimens from the Grotte de Coizard (Marne), the Grotte de Castellet, near Arles (Bouches-du-Rhône), Santa Cruz, California, where a cream-coloured point of jasper had penetrated the muscles of a man's back to sink deeply into the bone, and from a burial mound near Fort Wadsworth, Dakota, where a white quartz arrowhead was found lodged in a vertebra. The absence of any bony reaction around the injury shows that death followed rapidly, presumably from perforation of a large blood vessel or from its having penetrated the intestine before entering the bone. It was long ago proposed that the frequency with which the lumbar vertebrae were wounded is due to the relative softness of their cancellous bodies in contrast to the tougher cervical and thoracic segments. This may be so but it also suggests that shields were carried or armour worn which may have protected the upper part of the torso. It is a truism which tends to be ignored by archaeologists that no bone can be directly wounded by any weapon unless soft tissues have first been sectioned and to assess the consequences of any skeletal wound it is essential to visualize what injury to other structures preceded it. In the Téviec instance quoted above death must have occurred at once: to come to rest where it did the flint would have had to cut clean through the main thoracic aorta.

Plates 18, 19   Many similar examples are known. In another case from the Grotte de la Lave (Vaucluse) a sacrum has been wounded posteriorly from the right but here the overlying tissues contain no structure of vital importance and recovery might be expected. Examination of the bone does indeed show ample healing round the arrowhead, the barb of which remained embedded in the sacrum after the tang had been snapped off, probably as a result of efforts to tug the arrow free. Sometimes the position or depth of penetration suggests, as in a skeleton from Villevenard, that the embedded flint was a spear tip which had been thrust into the victim rather than an arrowhead. Another reason for the fewer thoracic vertebrae that are wounded must be the protection afforded by the rib cage as can be seen in the neolithic man from Wor barrow, Dorset, with a leaf-shaped flint between his ribs or a Patagonian in whom the missile had stuck in the breast bone.

The early history of ballistics is faithfully mirrored in the injuries sustained by skeletal remains. We have already men- tioned Peruvian sling-shot wounds. The stones which caused them are usually about 35 mm. in diameter; the injuries are almost always well healed. A somewhat similar but more severe injury is also found among these people. It consists of a peculiar double or triple depressed fracture of the cranial vault which can be explained by their use of 'star-headed' maces as a favourite weapon. For medieval times the recorded descriptions of military weapons are confirmed by skeletal finds; the warrior graves from the battle of Visby (1361) yield examples of cross- bow bolts wedged in bones. And coming to much later times

Fig. 9

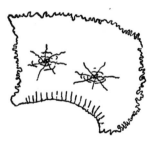

Fig. 9. Peruvian star-shaped mace-head, Precolumb- ian, and its typical skull wound.

49

the British Museum has an early example of an American Indian with a gun-shot buried in his face and surrounded by well-healed bone. The distribution of injuries may throw light on fighting techniques and the kind of armour used. Hundreds of sword cuts occur on the limb bones of the men who fought at Visby but only 15 per cent are found on the arms. Clearly this suggests that their greaves were less protective than the armour or shield with which they guarded the upper limbs but there are also reasons for thinking that the Danish invaders used a method of attack in which their second blow was regularly aimed at the Gotlanders' legs. The majority of these injuries occur on the left side of the body and this is partly due to the fact that an attacker would normally be right-handed and partly because the defender usually fought with his left leg in advance. Some especially severe wounds were probably the result of striking an already fallen adversary or of using a heavy two-handed sword. In either case the effect of right-handedness is obscured and wounds of this type are in fact found with equal frequency on both sides. A form of multiple, penetrating wound of the head occurs in these bodies that may be due to the weapons usually known by the charming name of 'morning stars'. These consisted of a handle and chain to which was attached a wooden ball studded with metal spikes; it was whirled round and brought down upon the victim's skull, a meteoric version of the Peruvian star-headed mace.

Plate 20

Weapon wounds could form the subject of a long treatise but it is perhaps more interesting to consider the kinds of injury that are due to factors of occupation or environment. No one has yet identified an injury caused by a Gaulish mowing machine though they may have been common enough, but in many communities well-defined fracture patterns occur and it is always rewarding to discover the reason for them. In excavating Anglo-Saxon burial grounds we often find fractures of the legs. Sometimes the tibia and fibula are both broken,

Fig. 10. Sites of injury in a Pott's fracture of the leg.

sometimes only one of them—usually the fibula. This particular type of fracture is characteristic of a fall in which the foot is twisted on the leg. It can occur in tripping over a city kerbstone and among the Saxons its frequency may be due to their work as agriculturists. Breaking and cropping rough ground prob-ably led to many a stumble with a Pott's fracture, a snapped fibula, as a result. Possibly clumsy footwear was a contributory cause. That such falls were common finds additional support from the great frequency of Colles' fractures in these people. This is a fracture of the forearm about an inch away from the wrist which is typically produced by falling forward on to an

Fig. 10

Fig. 11

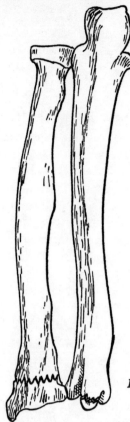

Fig. 11. Sites of injury in a Colle's fracture of the forearm.

outstretched hand. We, ourselves, are so accustomed to leg and
arm injuries of this kind, which are seen in hundreds at any
orthopaedic clinic, that it seems reasonable to suppose that they
must have been common in all people at all times. The facts
are otherwise. Among the ancient Egyptians broken arms far
outnumbered broken legs. In a series of nearly six thousand
Nubians ranging in date from predynastic to Byzantine times
only 10 per cent of all fractures were in the leg as compared
with 30 per cent in the forearm. One reason for this may have

been that the farm land these people worked was less rough and furrowed than that of the British Saxons. Much more important is the fact that they habitually went bare-footed. This gave them an intimacy of contact, a delicate awareness of the ground, which is denied to the hobnailed feet of legionaries and ceorls. Amongst these same Nubians were six examples of separation of the head of the thigh bone and six femoral neck fractures, injuries which in young people such as these usually result from severe falls. All except one of these cases occurred in a community of Christians who regularly wore boots (as was shown by the recovery of several bodies with them on) and who, moreover, inhabited two rocky and boulder-strewn islands in the Nile where craggy paths made walking a perilous event for people whose trammelled feet were divorced from close perception of the ground they trod.

It was suggested above that the occurrence of fractured arms among the Anglo-Saxons was proof of their proclivity to fall. The frequency of broken arms among the Egyptians might therefore be construed as rebutting the inference that these barefoot people seldom stumbled. No such conclusion can properly be reached. The majority of the Nubian fractures are quite unlike the 'accidental' Colles' type. They are lower or mid-shaft fractures of the ulna, or ulna and radius, of a kind which is typically the result of guarding the head against a blow. They point to short tempers and aggressive conduct being a common feature of the society and as many of them occur in females wife-beating or a generally low status of women may be implied. The mummy of a teenage girl has been found in which both forearms had been shattered in this way. When her efforts to protect her head proved unavailing her skull was crushed with a powerful blow. The fact that she was four or five months pregnant might have been the motive for this assault upon her. Despite these products of aggression, the over-all incidence of fractures amongst these people was low,

Fig. 12

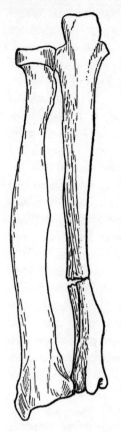

Fig. 12. Common site of injury in a 'parry' fracture of the forearm.

only about 3 per cent, whereas in the Anglo-Saxons almost 20 per cent of individuals had some bone broken though few of them could be attributed to personal violence and bickering.

A somewhat similar pattern of fractures to that of the Egyptians has been found in skeletons of several hundred pre-white Australian aborigines. Here again was a people who walked foot-free and unshod and no cases of Pott's, Colles' or femoral neck fractures were found. Parry fractures of the forearm were common, however, and their firm repair in good position hints at a knowledge of splinting. In some tribes who practised extensive wallaby-hunting over boulder-strewn terrain, broken legs and arms were not uncommon. Another apparently bare-footed group were the people who lived in about the time of Periclean Athens at Bodega Head, California, forty-five miles north of the Golden Gate. Amongst these folk Colles' fractures and fractures of the small bones of the lower limb were common, especially in males. This probably reflects a sexual division of labour in which the men scrambled over slippery rocks amid the surf and scud of the foreshore in search of the molluscs and small fish which were their staple diet whilst the women restricted their food gathering to more accessible pools left by the ebbing tide. Injuries due to personal violence are not identifiable here.

The varying incidence of 'aggression fractures' is an interesting comment on the social behaviour of different populations. In many peoples who are known from their history to have been warlike and truculent these fractures are surprisingly uncommon. This may mean that the group as a whole unleashed enough of its hostile impulses in forays against neighbouring tribes to have no need to quarrel amongst themselves. The Anglo-Saxons have already been noted as coming in this category; ancient Iranians from Tepe Hissar, pre-European Hawaiians, a group from Franc d'Ennery of the time of Clovis, and some of the early Peruvians give a similar picture. By contrast the American Indians of Pecos Pueblo show a high proportion of head injuries which were presumably acquired in brawls, though some of them may have resulted from houses collapsing upon their occupants, an event which on archaeological evidence seems to have been common.

The ability to survive an injury is closely related to its severity and the study of ancient trauma gives some clue to the resilience of early man. Simple fractures of the limbs are unlikely to have lethal results and almost all are found solidly healed even when the alignment of the bone is bad. Cranial fractures are much more serious and we can only marvel at the high recovery rate which is often found, especially in cases where surrounding inflammation of the bone shows that an open scalp wound became infected. Some peoples seem to have had a high resist~ ance to bacterial invasion. The Balboa Park series of Peruvian skulls which are peppered with sling~shot fractures shows little evidence of infection although the scalp was probably split open more often than not. The reason for this is uncertain. It suggests that efficient surgical treatment had been evolved with the use of some sort of antiseptic dressing. It is also likely that these communities enjoyed a level of diet which was high enough to let them maintain a good resistance to the stress of their environment. In primitive tribes where the primping and washing of hair claims a high place in the affairs of the toilet the cleanliness of the scalp reduces the chance of suppuration in wounds. No such factor can account for the relative immunity of the Peruvians; in the dishevelled tresses of their mummies (and one has been found with hair more than seven feet long) nits and lice are plentiful.

Plate 22

Many examples have been found in which two or more vertebrae have been telescoped together as a result of a crushing injury to the spine. The danger of this lesion is compression or tearing of the spinal cord with inevitable paralysis of the body below the site of injury. Until recent years this was probably always fatal from paralysis of the bladder with ascending infec~ tion of the kidneys, but in the absence of transection of the cord healed cases have been found in many burial grounds. An example of the ability to survive extensive injury is seen in a Romano~Briton from Snodland, Kent. This man had a broken collar~bone, together with six rib fractures on his right side and ten on his left. An injury of this kind could only result from severe crushing of the thorax. Laceration of the pleural cavity, lungs and pericardium, with possible rupture of liver or spleen, would be a likely concomitant with early death from haemorrhage or septic pneumonia. Yet this man survived his seventeen separate fractures although cross-fusion of several ribs and ossification of torn ligaments greatly reduced the original elasticity of his thoracic skeleton.

In many ancient texts including the Code of Hammurabi, the Edwin Smith surgical papyrus and the works of Galen, Paulus Aegineta, Avicenna and Haly Abbas, the treatment of fractures is mentioned, though they tell us little about the relative frequency of different kinds. The excavation of actual specimens gives a chance to see how successful the primitive surgeon was when he translated precept into practice. Movement across the broken ends of a large arm or leg bone can be so exquisitely painful that support and immobilization of the limb are demanded spontaneously by the patient. It is safe to assume therefore that splinting was devised early in the course of human history and splints of palm frond have in fact been found in ancient Egypt as early as the V Dynasty, whilst examples made of hide and clay are known respectively from North America and Australia. But it is axiomatic in treating fractures that it is useless to splint severely displaced fragments of bone until they have been reduced as nearly as possible to their normal position. If on the other hand the fragments are not initially displaced, no further harm is likely to come from leaving them unsupported. The great number of broken bones recovered from ancient sites leaves little doubt that whether or not splinting was used the early surgeons had negligible skill in the reduction of fractures. Few convincing exceptions are found and this is not surprising in view of the fact that apart from any anatomical knowledge that may be required it is usually necessary, even today, to give the patient an anaesthetic in order to overcome the powerful muscle spasms which accompany a fractured humerus or femur and make reduction almost impossible even for an expert surgeon. Percival Pott

Plate 21

(1714–88), the eponym of the fracture, seems to have been the first surgeon explicitly to state the importance of relaxed muscles in the treatment of broken bones. Many ancient fractures, though firmly united with great masses of new bone, are appallingly deformed and it seems certain that until recently surgeons had little skill in setting a broken limb. That a well-healed fracture need not imply any treatment at all is shown by Schultz's work on the spontaneous repair of broken bones in gibbons and the many human fractures which have united in almost perfect alignment have done so despite surgical intervention, not because of it.

A few other injuries from physical causes attracted the attention of early writers. Hippocrates in *Airs, Waters, Places* discusses sunstroke and the susceptibility of elderly people to it. Celsus refers to the stupefaction or stunning (*attonitas*) of those struck by lightning. Penal mutilation or death is often suspected but seldom proved. A possible case of early medieval date is that of a man found at Géronde, Sierre. Under the Burgundian *lex Gundobada* several crimes were punishable by cutting off the hand and this person had a double mutilation; both forearms were amputated in their lower thirds and both had cleanly healed. At Aebelholt, Denmark, a peculiar unilateral inflammation just above the ankle in four bodies could have been caused by prison shackles. A few Peruvian portrait vases may be intended to represent penal slitting of the nose. All these are uncertain. Quite different are the remains of over a hundred men of the Roman period found near Shellal in Nubia. They had all been hanged after having their arms and legs lashed together. In many of them the sutures at the base of the skull were dragged open and an asymmetrical distortion produced but the reason for this is not clear. The one-sided gaping of the sutures looks as though it was caused by the knot in the rope yet it is a lesion that is unknown in modern judicial hanging. Why this mass execution took place remains a mystery but the victims show traces of negroid admixture that set them apart from their Egyptian neighbours and they may have been Blemmyes, nomads of the Eastern desert, who were harrying the Romans at that time.

Finally there are the remarkable bog-burials of northern Germany, Denmark and Holland. About a hundred have been recovered, men and women in almost equal numbers. They mostly fall within the millennium 500 B.C.–A.D. 500 and though a few may be due to casual accident or foul play, there is strong evidence that many of them were sacrifices to a vegetation goddess or some similar divinity. Late Bronze or Iron Age torcs are often found in these bogs, apparently as deliberate offerings, and both the Tollund and Borremose men had been strangled with nooses twisted into a close likeness of this kind of torc. The wholly vegetarian stomach contents of the Tollund and Grauballe men (the latter had a cut throat) may indicate that their last meal was a sacramental repast connected with a vegetation fertility rite.

Plate 23

DEGENERATIONS

This strange disease of modern life.
MATTHEW ARNOLD

Trauma, infection and deficiency diseases have a gratifying precision as causes of pathological change. Conditions des- cribed as 'degenerative' are much less understood but are none the less important because among them is osteoarthritis which has the distinction of being one of the commonest, most wide- spread and most antique of all diseases. Before we discuss its incidence and significance, however, a brief description of it will not come amiss. Osteoarthritis is an affection of joints, especially the large joints in limbs and those between the arti- cular processes of vertebrae—but none are exempt except fixed synarthroses such as the sutures of the skull. In simple

Fig. 13. *Articular condyles of the lower jaw. a. normal; b. flattened by osteoarthritis.*

terms it leads to a degeneration and erosion of the cartilage that covers the opposed surfaces of bone and to destruction or reactionary proliferation of the bone itself. Its cause is not fully known; endocrine and metabolic dyscrasias probably play a part but injury, especially repeated episodes of minor stress, is the most important single factor in its onset and in determining the joints it will attack. We have already seen how fractures betray the thrust and shear of major occupational hazards. Osteoarthritis also does this; but whereas a fracture records an isolated event arthritic changes tend rather to register the cumulative effect of strain over many years. The well-healed break in a neolithic mandible from Vaudancourt is proof of a sudden

Fig. 13

blow on the jaw; the arthritic mandibular condyles of an elderly Saxon from Burgh Castle reinforce the evidence of dental attrition to disclose a lifelong habit of chewing tough, smoked or salted meat and munching crusty bannocks baked from grit-laden flour. Osteoarthritis and fractures are therefore complementary sources for assessing environmental stress.

Two other conditions must be mentioned here because they are often confused with osteoarthritis and, despite striking clinical and pathological differences, are presumably related to it albeit to an extent that is by no means clear. The first is rheumatoid arthritis which is the local expression of a generalized disorder loosely associated with rheumatism—whatever that may be. It typically affects multiple small joints and although it starts in the synovial membrane it involves the periarticular ligaments and capsule more than the internal cartilage. It appears to be one of the recently defined 'auto-immune' diseases such as lupus erythematosus or Hashimoto's thyroiditis in which the body reacts adversely to antigens of its own making. The second is osteophytosis. This is the name given to jagged excrescences of bone in the joints of limbs or between the bodies of the vertebrae. It is a gonfalon of other pathological processes, not a disease in its own right, but if severe it can fuse several spinal segments into a single rigid column producing what is often called 'bamboo' or 'poker' spine, although this term is usually reserved for ankylosing spondylitis in which there is ossification of the longitudinal ligament. Chronic strain contributes to the onset of vertebral osteophytosis, particularly compression of the backbone from humping heavy loads, but the over-all shrinkage and loss of elasticity in the intervertebral discs as age advances is also connected with it in some way. We need not be surprised that there is a general tendency to mistake one of these conditions for another since there is both a similarity and a relationship between them. Unfortunately the confusion is made worse by the bedlam of nomenclature that infests the literature. Osteoarthritis is commonly encountered in the guise of arthritis deformans (after Virchow), whilst proliferating arthritis, nodular rheumatism, dry arthritis, rheumatic gout, rheumatoid arthritis and morbus senilis are other names used to denote it. Osteophytosis is often called spondylitis deformans, vertebral spondylitis and osteoarthritis whilst eponymous terms such as Strümpell-Marie disease add to the chaos until, in the absence of photographs or an adequate definition, it is frequently impossible to decide what the author is writing about. With the caveat of this preamble in mind we can now review some of the ancient evidence of these conditions.

Plate 24

The earliest examples of osteoarthritis occur in dinosaurs, in which it has even been mistaken for tuberculosis; various joints are affected and vertebral osteophytosis is also found.

Thereafter it remains a common condition. Coalesced verte-brae have been recorded in a Lower Miocene gavial (*Tomistoma dowsoni*), a Cuban crocodile and in many Pleistocene specimens including the cave bear, cave hyena, *Bos primigenius* and other animals. This wide generic distribution is demonstrated still further by the recognition of spinal changes in sacred monkeys from Egyptian temples near Thebes and also in the sheep and oxen of dynastic times. It is common in the Equidae, amongst which it has been discovered to affect the dorsal region of the spine in pre-Roman wild horses whereas in modern riding and working horses it is the lumbar region which is attacked. This contrast must certainly be due to a difference in the focus of stress between the two groups, and a similar disparity for man has been noted: in modern Swedes and Americans the last lumbar vertebra is the one most commonly involved by osteo-phytosis but in a thousand prehistoric spines the nub of inci-dence was the middle lumbar region.

This twin complex of osteoarthritis and osteophytosis is common among the Neandertals. The jaw is especially prone to be attacked, as in the individuals from Krapina, La Ferrassie, La Quina and La Chapelle-aux-Saints, and since the joint is often affected at an early age we can assume that they fed on a tough, perhaps uncooked, diet and put their jaws to vigorous use gnawing bones, cracking nuts and champ-ing roots. The La Chapelle skeleton also had extensive vertebral changes, and these were destined to have far-reaching effects because it was the reconstruction of this specimen which gazetted the view that the Neandertals groped their way through a hundred thousand years of prehistory in a semi-erect posture. It is clear that this old gentleman did walk with a pronounced stoop as many old men with his degree of spinal curvature do today, but those of us who are still lithe and sprightly have no wish to be equated with our decrepit elders and it is unfair to the rest of the Neandertals to judge them by this singularly pathological example: there is ample evidence that they were an erect and lissom people.

In many groups these bony changes are the most important lesions to survive. The ancient Egyptians were much afflicted with osteophytosis; at all periods from predynastic to Roman times about half the adults over the age of twenty-five developed it and they were attacked severely and relatively often in their thoracic segments. Recent work which has established that the lower lumbar region is the site of election in modern European populations provokes enquiry into the cause of this difference. Several reasons contribute to the explanation; one is body-weight. The combined mass of the head, arms and trunk may account for three-quarters of the total weight of the body and this load is transmitted downwards through the spinal column. The vertebrae of the neck support only the head and part of the suspension of the shoulder girdle, a burden which is seldom excessive. But the fifth lumbar vertebra with its adjoining discs may, in an obese man, sustain a perpendicular thrust of ten or twelve stone or more, and though corpulent persons do appear in the mummies of pharaonic times the average ancient Egyptian was slimmer and lighter than the average German, Swede or American today. This may be one reason for the comparatively low incidence of fifth lumbar damage in the Nile valley fellahin. Another is that the Egyptian did not compress his lumbar discs by slouching in lounge chairs and limousines or by slumping over office desks.

In Anglo-Saxons the modern pattern is found with emphasis on low lumbar damage and this is even more obtrusive for arthritis than for osteophytosis. We can hardly doubt that the Saxons were a heavier people than the Egyptians, and this fits the suggested correlation between bone change and body weight. Their work as farmers, often breaking rough and pot-holed ground, must have increased the pivotal trauma in their lower spinal segments. In these people the women are afflicted equally with the men—as is bound to happen when the total frequency is nearly a hundred per cent—but in the Pecos Pueblo group, where less than one person in seven had the disease, males were attacked three times as often as females. This indicates a sexual division of occupations and may also imply a better relative status for the women. There is much to suggest that among Anglo-Saxons and at least the lower-class Egyptians women submitted to a great deal of oppressive drudgery and heavy physical work. The ancient Nubians had a very high incidence of osteoarthritis in the neck and this has led to the suggestion that it was a compression injury due to the habitual carrying of water-pots on the head. It is a neat expla-nation but rather too facile to be satisfying because extensive cervical disease also occurs in peoples who never carried burdens in that way. It was extremely common in the Late Medieval cemetery at Aebelholt, Denmark, and here Møller-Christensen has said that it was caused by dental caries and its concomitant jaw abscesses. He found the association so significant that he gave the name 'Aebelholt disease' to the dual condition, an innovation that seems too monopolistic in view of the fact that this relationship between oral infection and spinal change had already been observed in other early populations. Moodie long ago noticed it among the Peruvians, but the idea that dental sepsis begets disease in remote parts of the body is far older than either of these writers. One of the Assyrian letters in the Kuyunjik collection (eighth century B.C.) reads: '. . . the inflammation which grips the man's head and neck, and wrings the joints of his arms and legs, comes from his teeth. These teeth of his must be drawn. They are the root of his nagging pain. . . .'

Arthritis is often attributed to 'rheumatism' with the result that cold, damp climates are said to induce it. Its occurrence in ancient Nubians from Faras, one of the hottest and most arid places in the world, gives no support to this notion and, though much about the disease remains a mystery, as far as palaeopathology is concerned the theory of recurrent minor injury is the most rewarding. A few other examples will rein-force this view. From Chatby, near Alexandria, the remains of many of the Macedonian soldiers of Alexander the Great and Ptolemy I have been recovered. Degenerative diseases of bone and cartilage are abundant amongst them and one of the sites of election is the foot, in particular the first metatarsal. This is in contrast to the infrequency with which it attacks this region in native Egyptians and may be explained as a consequence of prolonged marching, sometimes with heavy equipment but above all in clumsy footwear. The early Patagonians had ex-tensive arthritis in the shoulder and elbows that has been interpreted as due to the peculiar stresses imposed by their use of the bola as a hunting weapon; the rotational movement necessary to hurl the stones is one which concentrates the strain at these joints. Prehistoric skeletons from West and South African sites have been found with lipping of the small bones in the wrist and at the base of the right thumb. The cause of this seems to be the repeated jarring or concussion of these joints in people who hacked at sun-roasted soils with hoe and mattock. The eleventh-century Transvaal group from Bamban-dyanalo were pastoralists who did not practise hoe culture, and their hands were unaffected by arthritic lesions. It has even been suggested that osteophytosis in the spine of a Minoan skeleton was the result of a compression injury whilst bull-leaping. That this man may have seen the myth of Theseus and Ariadne take shape in the lives of real men and women is remotely possible; that the blue anemone of death curled round his own eyelids in the anguish of the Labyrinth must be rejected as no more than the shadow of a fancy.

Apart from specifically localized areas of osteoarthritis deter-mined by occupational trauma there is a broader relationship between this disease and the general standard of living. Other things being equal, when the over-all stress of life eases for a people they tend to be less afflicted with it. The ancient Greeks demonstrate this succinctly. In the Neolithic and early Bronze Age they were inefficient hoe farmers who lived on lentils, cereals, acorns, almonds, peas, herbs and a few wild, as well as domesticated, animals. Their diet was adequate, had some graces such as figs, truffles and oysters, but yielded little surplus. By the late Bronze Age (the Mycenaean period) irrigation, manuring, crop rotation and above all the introduction of the plough from Crete, though not greatly extending the range ot foods available, had permitted a higher individual consumption until the banquets of the wine-swigging, beef- and cheese-gorging Homeric heroes became, if not commonplace, at least a practical possibility for festive occasions rather than the hungry dream of a half-starved poet. With this improvement in nutrition not only is there an increase in stature, longevity and population but also a decline in the amount of arthritis.

In a previous section it was argued that the pattern of fractures found in the Bodega Head Californians was due to falls on slippery foreshore rocks. In addition to a high proportion of lumbo-sacral and sacro-iliac arthritis which may have been produced in the effort to maintain balance they show an un-usual amount of this condition in the knee and foot. Probably some of their knee disease was the result of a torn semilunar cartilage—an injury all too familiar to footballers and other athletes today. Often in cases of this kind the erosion of cartilage and internal destruction of the joint is so severe that the exposed bones grind against each other and develop a chafed or Plate 26 'eburnated' surface like polished ivory. This is seen in the hips of the La Chapelle-aux-Saints Neandertal. A joint in this state cripples the victim with pain and reduces his life to one of misery and wretchedness, but the disease can progress still further and lead to ankylosis, or complete fusion of the bones. When this happens the joint becomes rigid and immovable but often ceases to be painful so that the limb as a whole can again be used. Many ankylosed joints have been recorded from the Neolithic period onwards but a number of these are due to infection or badly united fractures.

Plate 25

A few other skeletal degenerations are occasionally met in the burial grounds. Perthes' disease of the hip is one. Its cause is uncertain but when severe it destroys the head of the thigh bone together with its socket and cripples the limb. A medieval man with this condition from Thetford, Norfolk, had un-availingly sought relief in supplication to Our Lady of Rocama-dour (Lot). A pilgrim's badge testifying to his visit to the shrine lay beside him in his grave.

Plate 27

In clinical practice today the degenerative lesions of soft tissues are common and important. The best known is arterio-sclerosis, or hardening of the arteries, which is often said to be due to the pressure of modern life together with tobacco smoking and the cocktail habit. This explanation, however deft, is unconvincing because the disease is widespread in Egyptian mummies. These people knew nothing of tobacco and, though far too gracious to be teetotallers, they certainly did not mess about with cocktails. As for the pressure of life, no doubt it trailed many anxious moments for those involved with the Hyksos expulsion or the palace intrigues of the Ramesside period but it can hardly have been lived at the pace of Broadway. One famous sufferer from arteriosclerosis was Rameses II, whose many blackheads suggest a dislike of washing; another was Mereneptah, the traditional pharaoh of the Exodus. His aorta, the main blood-vessel coming from the heart, was a perfect example of advanced arterial calcification: caprice and irascibility thrive on this pathology. Yet another example is a XXI Dynasty woman, Teye, from Deir-el-Bahri who had a calcified and thickened mitral valve in her heart, hardening of many arteries including her coronaries, and secondary fibrosis of her kidneys.

Thick and tortuous blood-vessels are often seen in radio-graphs of mummies where they provide further evidence of the antiquity of this so-called twentieth-century ailment. Recently A. T. Sandison has made a study of arterial disease in mummies and has succeeded in preparing brilliant microscopical sections of the degenerated tissues.

Plates 28, 29

Arteriosclerotic changes of this kind frequently herald cerebral catastrophes such as a hemiplegia or stroke. When this happens unilateral paralysis is likely to follow. An intra-cranial accident of this kind can be diagnosed in a female mummy of the Persian period, fifth century B.C., who had a facial asymmetry. Literary evidence suggests that strokes were well known in the ancient world: the Berlin medical papyrus (*c.* 1300 B.C.) appears to describe a paralysed face when it says, 'A fumigation for curing a contortion of half of his face and the angle of his mouth. Fumigate the patient over the smoke of wood chips; dose him with sweet ales until he sweats abundantly; then massage him with the hand.' An Assyrian medical text prescribes pigeons' droppings, wax and fat of opopanax 'if a man's mouth troubles him, it being distorted to the right so that he cannot utter his words or control his speech', and the Hippocratic *Prorrhetikon* says, 'Contortions of the face which are unconnected with anything else in the body clear up quickly, with or without treatment; otherwise they are apoplectic.' Many similar references to cerebral seizures are scattered throughout the classical medical writings. Among the Iroquois of North America masks of twisted faces are common and it is often assumed that they represent the effects of a stroke or other type of palsy. But these tribes had an important social institution known as 'The False Face Society' whose members wore grotesque masks, and the carvings should not be regarded as intentional representations of disease. Very

Fig. 14

different from these is a Tlingit helmet carved in the likeness of an old man with facial paralysis. No similar society existed

Fig. 14. Tlingit wooden helmet in the form of a man with facial paralysis.

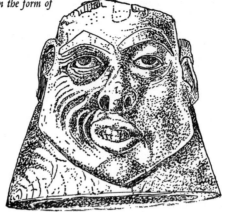

among these Pacific coast people and the helmet can be accepted as a lifelike piece of portraiture. Arteriosclerosis has also been found in Peruvian mummies but less commonly than with the Egyptians. Even so, we might surmise that strokes were occasionally produced by it and Mochica vases exist which support this view. Masks from Africa and Asia give further evidence of the wide distribution of this kind of arterial hardening.

Plate 30

Plates 31, 32

Three more degenerative conditions may be briefly noted. The lung diseases silicosis and anthracosis which are due respectively to the irritation of inhaled dust and carbon or coal have both been detected in Egyptian mummies, as also has emphysema, a degeneration and destruction of the elastic tissue of the lungs. It can result from asthma or chronic bronchitis and is characteristic of persons who strain the lung by playing wind musical instruments or singing too forcibly. It was found in the mummy of Har-mose, a fat singer of the XVIII Dynasty, who died of acute broncho-pneumonia and pleural effusion.

This brief survey shows that degenerative diseases are not only among the commonest of any that we endure today but have also plagued man back to his emergence from the pre-hominids and many forms of life long before him. Some of them are among the most sensitive indicators of environmental stress and their varying incidence in time and place reveals a great deal about early patterns of human behaviour.

NEW GROWTHS

As quick a growth to meet decay.
ROBERT HERRICK

Neoplasms, or 'new growths' as they are commonly called, fall into two classes: benign and malignant. The discrimination is not, perhaps, valid in terms of basic cellular pathology. It is, however, clinically convenient and if the surgeon occasionally feels that the dividing line between them is somewhat blurred, the patient in suspense for the dreadful verdict sees the distinction as sharp as a lancet. Benign or 'innocent' growths are not only common, they are also sufficiently various in their presentation to appear even to lay eyes as a patchwork of unrelated diseases. Ordinary warts, nasal polyps, goitres, lipomata and uterine fibroids are all benign neoplasms. In contrast to these conditions people with no medical training surely think of malignant growths as constituting a single disease: cancer. Nothing could be further from the truth. Cancers are as protean in their behaviour and appearance as they are variable in prognosis. They range from some of the melanomata which are monotonously lethal to basal-celled carcinomata where the rule is very nearly 'cure guaranteed'. It is important to bear this in mind when discussing the subject of new growths.

Bones can be affected by three main kinds of neoplasm; osteoma, sarcoma and carcinoma. Simple or 'ivory' osteoma, which is a benign condition, is by far the commonest of these. It is constantly found in early cemeteries from all over the world and often takes the form of a small hard knob about the size of

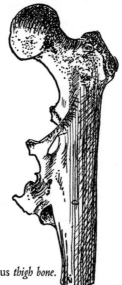

Fig. 15. Exostosis on the original Pithecanthropus erectus *thigh bone.*

a pea on the surface of the skull. They can, however, appear on any bone and are often multiple. A sixteenth-century Danish skeleton from Naestved had a hundred and thirty-four of them. These ivory osteomata are seldom much bigger than a walnut but another type may greatly exceed this and in some animals, especially the Bovidae where they tend to arise from the cranial sinuses, they may weigh a dozen pounds or more. In a medieval human skull from Var, France, a huge osteoma of this kind obliterated a large part of the cranial cavity. These tumours have a long history, having been described in mososaurs and cave bears, but their diagnosis is difficult and they are especially liable to be confused with simple exostoses which are not primarily growths but are reactions to injury or irritation. The craggy mass of bone on the proximal end of the *Pithecanthropus erectus* femur is probably of this type. A tibial exostosis from a dolmen at Saint-Affrique (Aveyron) has developed around a flint arrowhead which is embedded in the

Plate 33

Fig. 15

bone, and one on the foot of a fifth-century Copt has been diagnosed as due to wearing tight boots. A process of ossification invading tendons and muscles is similar to these reactionary exostoses. It is a common condition in the bipedal dinosaurs such as *Diplodocus* as well as in the Ceratopsians and is also found in the Felidae, as for example in the Oligocene and Miocene fossil *Daphoenus*. An interesting form of these innocent growths occurs in the bony canal leading down to the ear-drum. It is met sporadically in most populations but the American Indians are especially subject to it, some groups having an incidence of almost 100 per cent. They may be single or multiple and range in size from a pin-head to a mass which completely blocks the passage and must greatly reduce the acuity of hearing. A few other benign neoplasms are found some of which are, or point to, lesions of the soft tissues. Derry has described an ancient Egyptian skull in which a hole about one inch in diameter was present in the right parietal. The bone around this opening was slightly depressed and he thought the condition was due to pressure from a dermoid cyst. A female Nubian mummy of Byzantine date has been found with a fibrous vaginal polyp and another of the same period with a vaginal cyst. The Kahun papyrus (*c.* 1900 B.C.) refers to prolapse of the uterus: 'in the case of a woman with backache and a dragging down feeling between her thighs, tell her it is a dropped womb.' Greek medical texts also discuss it and their surgeons even treated it by hysterectomy—removal of the organ. Terracotta models of these excised wombs are found as votive offerings brought by grateful patients to Asklepios, the god of healing. Plate 34 shows an Etruscan example on which there is a cyst or polyp that may have played a part in the development of just such a prolapse.

Plate 34

Benign growths are therefore well attested in many forms from early populations and their frequency may have been about the same as it is today, but when we turn to malignant tumours a totally different situation is found. Of the two common forms of skeletal cancer, sarcoma and carcinoma, the first is a primary growth of osseous tissue which starts in a bone and spreads into surrounding organs, the second invariably begins in epithelial tissue such as a gland or mucous membrane and only invades bone as a secondary and late event in its career. The fact that sarcomata originate in a bone makes it likely that they will survive inhumation and many have done so. What is perhaps the first palaeopathological specimen to be recorded was described by E. J. C. Esper in 1774 as a femoral sarcoma in a cave bear: it was later shown to be callus round a fracture. But undoubted examples, also in *Ursus spelaeus*, have been found at the Grotte du Dragon, Mixnitz, Austria, and elsewhere. One of the earliest human cases to be described was in the thigh bone of a V Dynasty Egyptian. A few others have also been found there and they occur too in ancient Peruvian skulls. Moodie has interpreted some of these as extensions from a specific type of intracranial tumour known as a meningioma but this seems merely to reflect the fashion of medical opinion at the time he wrote. In the first quarter of the twentieth century dramatic advances in brain surgery were made by Harvey Cushing whose bold attack on these tumours gripped the scientific imagination no less than it amazed the man in the street.

It is with carcinoma that the greatest difference is found between modern and ancient patterns of malignant disease. Today the common carcinomata—cancer of the stomach, bowel, lung, breast, uterus and many other organs—kill millions of people every decade. Evidence of the disease from early burial grounds is rare. No simple explanation of this is possible. One reason must be that cancer chiefly attacks the elderly. In early populations the average age at death was well short of that time of life when the disease attains a dominant place in the tables of mortality. But some people did survive to become senile and plenty of cancers occur today in middle-aged or even young adults, so it seems that some other explana-tion is needed to account for only two or three cases having been found in all the tens of thousands of Egyptian mummies and skeletons which have been examined. Perhaps the close contact of later urban life permitted a virus element to play a part.

Early literary sources are equally unrewarding. Herodotus relates that Atossa, who was the wife of Darius and by far the most celebrated woman in the ancient history of Persia, had a swelling on her breast which burst through the skin and grew progressively larger until it was treated and cured by the Greek surgeon Democedes. Reckless scholiasts have assumed that she had a cancer but this diagnosis is quite untenable and it was clearly a form of inflammatory mastitis. Hippocrates prob-ably has true cancer in mind when he says (*Aphorisms VI*: 38) that patients live longer if physicians make no attempt to treat them. If so, Paulus Aegineta (A.D. 625–90) was prepared to ignore the advice since he describes operative removal of the breast but, like Galen before him, fails to distinguish clearly between benign and malignant processes. Ts'ang Kung, the great physician of the Han dynasty (206 B.C.–A.D. 220) records carcinoma of the stomach.

Only a handful of indubitable cases can be identified from ancient remains. Both the Egyptian specimens recorded by Elliot Smith were of Byzantine date; one was a carcinoma of the rectum, the other a growth of the naso-pharynx. This is of quite exceptional interest because a recently identified specimen dating from the Pyramid Age of the Old Kingdom is a perfect example of a primary naso-pharyngeal cancer which by secon-dary deposits had eroded more than a dozen holes through the vault of the skull. Apart from a most improbable case at Maiden Castle, Dorset, one of the few likely specimens from the Old World is from the fourth-millennium B.C. Iranian site

Plate 35

of Tepe Hissar; this, too, is a naso-pharyngeal lesion. In another, from Chavina, Peru, the palate and the walls of the maxillary sinus have been destroyed by a growth in a closely similar fashion to the specimen shown in Plate 34. Cancers in this part of the body are relatively rare in America and Western Europe today but in parts of Africa they are the commonest of all malignant growths and are often present in children or teenagers. Whether this is due to dust in the air, smoking habits, a virus factor, time spent over a charcoal fire or genetic predisposition is unknown. Nor is it possible to decide what connection if any exists between the modern and the ancient examples, but the parallel is impressive in view of the highly specialized agents each of which is known to initiate a different kind of malignant growth. The problem is made still more complicated by recent African discoveries that point unmistakably to trace elements in the soil and to insect vectors as being somehow involved in the genesis or spread of some kinds of cancer. It is not surprising that the early history of this disease is difficult to unravel when even now it is so ill understood. Few people learn without surprise that in Great Britain today cancer is the most frequent cause of natural death in children between the ages of one and fourteen years.

Myelomatosis, an unusual form of growth in which multiple deposits occur in bone, has been recognized in two pre-columbian Indians, an old man found on the south bank of the Susquehannah River close to Binghampton and a ten-year-old child near Rochester, both in New York State. Further cases come from an Early Bronze Age Pyrenean site and from medieval England. One other possible example of very ancient malignancy is the Kanam mandible, which has a large neoplastic tumour of the chin. It has been diagnosed as a sarcoma but its precise status is doubtful.

Finally, we may linger over a piece of sculpture from the classical world which illustrates the pitfalls inherent in this type of evidence when it is interpreted in ignorance of the artistic convention of the material or without regard to the scathe of centuries. In the Cesnola collection of Cypriot antiquities there is an ex-voto in the form of a woman's torso.

Plate 36

It has an irregularity of the stone below the breast that has been diagnosed as cancer, tuberculous ulceration of the skin and various other diseases. Only misguided enthusiasm could lead to such an opinion, which accords neither with the appearance of the 'lesion' nor with prevailing trends in the art of the period. The simple truth is that it is nothing more than the weathered remains of a bunch of grapes, complete with stalk, that the woman is clutching as a fertility symbol—a common enough motif in classical sculpture.

NON-SPECIFIC INFECTIONS

Here in the flesh, within the flesh, behind,
Swift in the blood and throbbing on the bone.

JOHN MASEFIELD

Non-specific infections are especially interesting; they are also among the least understood of ancient diseases. In contrast to specific infections where we can look at a lesion and say with confidence that it is due to tuberculosis or leprosy or polio-myelitis, a non-specific infection of necessity entails uncertainty. A bone with non-specific osteitis is one with inflammatory changes that could have been caused by a wide range of streptococcal, staphylococcal or other micro-organisms and the significance of which must therefore be doubtful. These conditions are important because of their great frequency in early cemeteries and although they are often difficult to interpret many of them reveal, with unusual clarity, occupational hazards and environmental influence.

One of the commonest lesions of this type is periostitis. This can be recognized by the fluted surface produced on a bone by

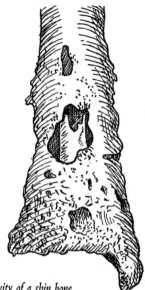

Fig. 16. Osteomyelitis (abscess formation) in the cavity of a shin bone.

inflammation of its covering membrane. It is often found as part of a more extensive infection (osteitis) or in conjunction with septic invasion of the marrow cavity (osteomyelitis). Non-specific infections of this kind have great antiquity; osteo-myelitis has been recognized in reptiles from the Permian epoch two hundred million years ago, in Cretaceous dinosaurs a hundred million years ago and in a Pleistocene lion (*Felis atrox bebbi*) and giant wolf (*Ænocyon dirus*). Periostitis occurs commonly in the cave bear (*Ursus spelaeus*) and in the sabre-tooth tiger (*Machairodus*), whilst in man it is frequently met from Neolithic times onward. It often results from injury, especially in bones that lie closely under the skin. The tibia is probably the most vulnerable site of all; the vault of the skull, though not deeply placed, is usually protected by a fell of hair and the toughness of the scalp. But even deep structures like

Fig. 16

the shaft of the femur can be affected and it is clear that many different factors can produce the condition—hence the term non-specific.

In a group of Saxon agriculturists about one in six had a tibial infection of this type. The high rate of fractured legs among these people has already been mentioned and this frequency of periostitis offers additional proof that their shins were much exposed to injury either as a result of the kind of tools they favoured or from the rough ground over which they worked. Another possibility is that these infections were produced by some sort of cross-gartered legging or buskin which chafed the skin and underlying tissues or by a habit of lacing their boots too tightly above the ankle. We know little about Anglo-Saxon footwear and further investigation of these points might be rewarding. In discussing fractures it was noted that compared with the Anglo-Saxons the Egyptians had a low incidence of broken legs. A similar freedom from tibial infections might also be expected but in fact the condition is equally common in the two peoples, and since the Egyptian injury rate, as measured by fractures, is so much less than that of the Saxons it appears that something other than trauma, or at least a different kind of injury, was responsible for their periostitis. In Egypt today, and presumably in Pharaonic times also, insect bites or trivial abrasions are prone to become infected and lead to extensive sores that ooze pus and serum for long periods. These purulent ulcers easily erode the periosteum and subjacent bone and may account for much of the periostitis which occurs in ancient Egyptian tibiae. Further support for this view is given by the medical papyri.

From the Nile valley it is interesting to turn to another arid region. The rarity of Pott's leg fractures in pre-European cemeteries of central Australia has already been mentioned; by contrast periostitis, not only of the tibia and fibula, but also of the femur and radius, is extremely common. It is, moreover, associated with an osteitis of a type that seems peculiar to the aborigines of this territory. The whole bone tends to be affected and although rarefaction and destruction are often present the outstanding feature is a dense sclerosing reaction of a kind hardly to be seen elsewhere. It has been thought that this condition is really due to trepenarid, which is a form of non-venereal syphilis, or to an unknown specific infection restricted to the area. Whatever the cause may be, an almost unparalleled frequency of osseous inflammatory change is met in these people: most long bones are affected and many skulls also. In some of the aborigines cranial infections were the result of an institutionalized custom of settling disputes by hitting each other alternately on the head.

Many other people display these damaged shin bones. In a group of Texas Indians dating from A.D. 800 onwards about a third of all tibiae were affected and this high incidence again seems to be due to a combination of agricultural injuries and climatic factors. A similar frequency in the Bodega Head people probably resulted from abrasions acquired when slithering about on slimy rocks in search of clams and edible sea-weed. Disorders of circulation account for a few of these non-specific infections of the leg. Varicose veins are strongly hereditary; they are also made worse by occupations that entail prolonged standing and by constricting fashions of dress. The narrow localization of some tibial lesions suggests that they were due to varicose ulcers that had gnawed deeply enough to expose the bone. Much variation is found in the degree to which bones, especially tibiae, are blemished by these infections. In some groups the inflammation was stubbornly chronic, in others where just as much infection is found healing occurred rapidly. The Bodega Head mussel and clam gatherers were among the latter, and this was probably due to the cleansing effect of saline irrigation as they puddled amongst the rock pools of the skerry. Elsewhere the availability of good materials for doctoring ulcers must often have determined how long they festered. Honey, which is still used in hospitals as a wound dressing, filled the bee-skeps of many ancient peoples; wine took the place of modern surgical spirit. Both were regularly used in the thera/ peutics of classical Greece. But there can be little doubt that other groups merely wrapped layers of filthy rag around dis/ charging sores and left them to stink undisturbed. Within these dressings pus formed and the tissues mortified into sloughs. Eventually maggots might hatch from the included eggs of blow/flies and once again modern treatment was simulated. Dominique Larrey, Napoleon's military surgeon, observed the beneficial effects of maggots, and in recent years ulcers and osteomyelitis have been treated with great success by deliberately introducing them into the wound. These creatures are sapro/ phytic. They live on dead, not living, tissue and after their regular use for a few days all necrotic debris and gangrenous shreds are eaten away leaving the flesh clean, healthy and ready for spontaneous healing. It is likely that many an ancient ulcer was successfully treated, albeit inadvertently, in this way.

Non/specific infections are not restricted to the long bones and the skull although they are most common in these sites. Infections by mixed organisms such as streptococci, diphthe/ roids, *Micrococcus catarrhalis* and many others often occur in the nose and throat from where they may spread to the sinuses, middle ear and mastoid air cells. Because sinuses are cavities within the bones of the skull evidence of sinusitis inside them is easily overlooked. Few workers have studied this disease in ancient skeletons although the condition is important on account of its far/reaching effects. When severe it is also likely to be chronic and the sinus or antrum will then contain a permanent sump of pus from which toxins permeate the body and lead to a general impairment of health. Descending infec/ tions of the respiratory tract that produce bronchitis and broncho/pneumonia are especially likely to develop from un/

Plates 38, 39

resolved sinusitis. This condition has been found with high frequency in Anglo-Saxons and Merovingians. In both these groups late childhood or adolescence were the healthiest periods in the life cycle and the rapid deterioration that often ensued once adult life was reached may have been largely the result of these descending infections from chronic disease of the frontal and para-nasal sinuses. What sinusitis implies presumably varies with different populations. Among both Anglo-Saxons and Merovingians its common occurrence may reflect the frequently inclement weather, winter-long nasal irritation from perpetually smouldering peat or log fires in ill-ventilated huts, and close-huddled living conditions in which droplet infection was readily spluttered from mouth to mouth. A like explanation probably holds good for the sinusitis which was common in the palaeolithic people who dwelt in a dank cave of the Gorges du Tarn at Baumes-Chaudes, Lozère. It is often found, too, in ancient Egyptians but with them its origin was certainly very different. Probably the dry, dust-laden air of the Nile valley produced a great deal of chronic nasal inflammation which inevitably extended to the sinuses. In addition to the dust that was inseparable from the climate of the country, vast numbers of the people were employed in producing more of it in the endless quarrying and building to which successive pharaohs committed each generation. In Bolivia and Peru sinusitis tends to be associated with fistula of the infected antrum and the severity of some cases appears to be related to the far-reaching effects of cranial deformation. There is also some evidence that the disease is common among people who used wind musical instruments. In Egypt these infections often spread from the nose to the ear and acute mastoid disease has been found in many bodies. This condition, which is commonly fatal, has already been mentioned in the archaic example of the Rhodesian skull. It has a wide distribution in space as well as time and is found in many different localities and

Plate 1

peoples. These include an Irish cairn at Knockast, medieval Burgundians, pre-white Queensland aborigines, an ancient Peruvian at Chicama, Aleutians, Greeks, Hittites and Ketchi-pauan fourteenth-century Pueblo dwellers.

Another disease that occasionally follows non-specific nasal infection is leontiasis, a 'lion-like' thickening of the bones of the head. The deformity can reach astonishing proportions. Vast masses of bone develop which obliterate the eye sockets and sinuses and change the delicate features of the skull into a shapeless horror of osseous tissue. The famous eighteenth-century Perpignan surgeon Fourcade had a son with this disease; when he died his lower jaw alone weighed 3 lb. 3 oz. (G.1586). Leonine indeed! Although a rarity, this condition also has a wide range: a good example has been found in a Peruvian site.

Plate 40

Many of these non-specific infections are due to fractures, either because the fracture was a compound one and the germs invaded the bone through a gash in the skin or, in simple fractures, because a stagnant clot of blood at the site of injury made a suitable incubator for blood-borne organisms. Perios-titis of the skull sometimes follows suppuration in a wen or tumour of the scalp: a possible example of this is an Anglo-Saxon from Mitcham, Surrey. These skull lesions are very common in ancient Egyptians, especially among the women, and it has been suggested that they are the result of wearing heavy wigs or more plausibly of carrying water-pots on the head.

Non-specific infections of soft tissues have been recognized in mummies. Broncho-pneumonia, which unlike lobar pneu-monia is not as a rule caused by the pneumococcus, has been found in an XVIII Dynasty Egyptian, another had pleurisy of unknown origin, yet another had appendicitis with perito-neal adhesions, and multiple kidney abscesses have been found. An old woman, Nesi-Tet-Neb-Taris, had a huge bedsore on her back which had been covered with a dressing of gazelle skin. The puerperal death of Queen Makere (XXI Dynasty) was probably due to generalized septicaemia but a few centuries later there is no need to speculate on the occurrence of puerperal infection: in the case books of Hippocrates, *Epidemics I and III*, brilliant descriptions of the condition are found which give a daily bulletin of the clinical progress.

Inflammation of hollow organs such as the gall-bladder, kidney pelvis and urinary bladder can result from a variety of pathogenic organisms and it sometimes happens that when this occurs shed epithelial cells form a nucleus around which calculi develop. Gall-stones, kidney and bladder stones have all been found in ancient Egyptians, the earliest in predynastic times, though they were undoubtedly rare. It is not easy to detect any reference to gall-stones in Egyptian or Greek medical texts but Galen describes them as being due to coagulation of the bile and Haly Abbas the Persian recorded them in the tenth century. Stone in the bladder is mentioned in the Hippocratic *Aphorisms*. Factors other than infection are probably equally important in producing these conditions. Gall-stones are influenced by diet. Urinary calculus seems closely linked to the type of water drunk; it was for several centuries the characteristic disease of East Anglia and the eighteenth-century Norfolk surgeons became highly skilled at cutting for it. For some reason that is one of the unexplained oddities in the history of disease it is much less common there today. An early American example of stone in the bladder (about 1000 B.C.) was recovered from the pelvis of a Basket Maker mummy; it was the size of a small pear and gave the normal chemical reactions of a urinary calculus. Stones due to infection or some other sort of irritation are probably of great antiquity since they affect many kinds of animals and appear in widely diverse forms. However unpalatable it may be to those with a distaste for the prosaic it remains a fact that the most lambent pearl ever to adorn a woman's breast was once an inflammatory secretion in a marine mollusc.

SPECIFIC INFECTIONS

> *If man could see*
> *The perils and diseases that he elbows,*
> *Each day he walks a mile.*

THOMAS LOVELL BEDDOES

A specific infection is one in which the disease is produced by a single type of organism and by that type only. There may be different varieties of the germ as in the human, bovine or avian strains of tuberculosis and the Flexner, Shiga or other breeds of the dysentery microbe, but each strain produces its distinct malady. Whereas non-specific infections such as broncho-pneumonia or cellulitis can be caused by many different germs, the specific infections of phthisis, syphilis and diphtheria can only result from infection by the *Mycobacterium tuberculosis*, *Treponema pallidum* and *Corynebacterium diphtheriae* respectively. There are very strong reasons for believing that in prehistoric times, until the Neolithic period when people began to crowd together in urban conditions, many of these diseases were either rare or had not even appeared as pathogenic to man. They made up for this later and became the great scourges of historic times. For at least two and a half millennia they have shaped the course of human destiny and played a greater part in the rise and fall of nations than all the tyrants and war-lords put together. Even the twentieth century has had its visitations. In 1943 Europe alone had a million cases in an epidemic of diphtheria gravis; in 1910–11 there were sixty thousand deaths from plague in Manchuria; in 1918–21 an estimated twenty-five million cases of typhus raged across Russia in the wake of the Revolution and of these probably three million died. Cholera, typhoid, dysentery and relapsing fever have each brought the embrace of death to untold numbers in our own times but all these diseases remained more or less localized even though their domain was a province or a continent. In 1918–19 the peak diffusion of all time was achieved by the world pandemic of influenza which killed more than twenty million people. Fortunately its mortality was far below that of the Black Death in the Middle Ages: had it not been, a thousand million people might have died.

This aspect of disease leads beyond the narrow corridor of human history into the consideration of infections as a cause of evolutionary change. In the last decade of the nineteenth century rinderpest exterminated vast herds of buffalo, gnu and giraffes in South Africa and *Trypanosoma brucei*, which is carried by *Glossina morsitans* and produces ngana or sleeping sickness, has destroyed numberless herds of horses and cattle. On the North American continent, horses existed up to the end of the tertiary epoch and it is quite possible that their disappearance may be a consequence of this disease: fossil tsetse flies of the Glossina genus have been identified in the Oligocene shales of Colorado.

Fig. 17

Fig. 17. Tsetse fly (Glossina morsitans) *found as an Oligocene fossil in Colorado. About* × 3½.

It is unfortunate for the palaeopathologist that most of the specific infections that have been the major epidemics of the past three thousand years leave no imprint on bones. This entails that their first appearance is uncertain and much of their early history obscure. We should like to know whether, as cuneiform records suggest, it was indeed smallpox which brought the Hittite empire to an end as it was later to devastate the Aztecs and toss the crown of Montezuma into the hands of the Conquistador; to know what part, if any, malaria played in the Manchu invasions of China; and whether cholera ever haunted dynastic Egypt.

For a brief review of some of these epidemics smallpox makes a good starting point because a case of it may be identifiable from early times. This is a XX Dynasty Egyptian mummy of a tall middle-aged man whose skin was covered with a dense vesicular eruption that had both the appearance and distribution of variola. Under the microscope the pustules were seen to be crowded with bacteria easily stainable by modern techniques, but as smallpox is caused by a virus which needs the electron microscope to reveal it these organisms were presumably a post-mortem invasion of saprophytes. A second possible case, also of the XX Dynasty, is the pharaoh Rameses V who had a similar rash on his face and pubic region. Despite much that has been written to the contrary, no scintilla of doubt should be left about the status of these diagnoses: in both examples it is a tentative suggestion, nothing more. They both look like smallpox and possibly are, but in mummified tissue the subtleties of diagnosis, not least of which is the clinical history of the case, elude the investigator and there is a bevy of other diseases with rashes like these to contest the field. Moreover, if they really were smallpox its fulminant infectivity might be expected to have produced far more examples in the large number of mummies that have survived.

There is one small point which has a general bearing on disease in ancient Egypt: many mummies, in spite of the appearance of emaciation that their dehydrated condition produces, were in reality plump or even corpulent persons at the time of death. This shows that they died of acute, not wasting, diseases.

Apart from this doubtful evidence from ancient Egypt we must depend on literary sources for what can be inferred about the early history of variola. Some of the oldest Sanskrit writings make it probable that it was endemic in India perhaps from the period of the Harappa and Mohenjo-Daro civilizations. In China hints of it are found at a similar date but it is only with Ko Hung (A.D. 281–361) that any physician gives a seemingly unequivocal account of it. He says, 'Recently many people have been afflicted with sores of the head, face and trunk which soon spread all over the body. These sores look like hot boils containing white matter. Whilst the first of these pustules are drying up fresh crops appear. Patients who survive are pock-marked with purple scars that take a year or more to fade.' He thought that it was introduced during the reign of Chien Wu when that king was fighting the Huns at Nang Yang, and says that the peasants dubbed it 'Hun pox'.

The Antonine Pestilence which swept the Roman empire in the second century A.D. was probably a mixture of infections with smallpox prominent among the diseases and Marcus Aurelius prominent among its victims. Desultory outbreaks, for example one in Abyssinia, kept the condition simmering during the fourth century. In A.D. 570 Bishop Marius of Lausanne and in A.D. 580 Gregory of Tours record epidemics of smallpox in France and Italy but it needed the Arab con-quests of the seventh century to disseminate it on the heroic scale and it was accurately described by Rhazes about A.D. 910. Thereafter it became established as a permanent disease in the Old World poised for invasion of the New. When it eventually struck the American mainland in 1520 it spread relentlessly and mauled the Indians so severely that some of the tribes, notably the Hurons, were almost wiped out by it.

Typhus, a louse-borne rickettsial disease, has been one of the great killers for at least five centuries but its early history is even more obscure than that of smallpox. It leaves no easily recog-nizable changes in the skeleton and neither mummies nor bones can be looked to as evidence of its presence in antiquity. It is probable but far from certain that the plague of Athens which swept the city in the second year of the Peloponnesian war was typhus: it has always been a fellow traveller of tick-bitten soldiers. Its absence from Roman records may be due to the popularity of bathing throughout the empire. In A.D. 217 the *Shang Han Lun* or 'Essay on Typhoid' was published. It is one of the masterpieces of Chinese medical literature and deals with many fevers in addition to typhoid; probably typhus is one of them but only at the end of the Middle Ages can we say for certain that it steps on to the stage of human epidemiology. When it does so it makes its début with éclat and a fanfare of trumpets in 1528 when Francis I laid siege to Naples, and again during the Thirty Years War.

Typhoid is no better documented, although Hippocrates described a fever attended with watery stools, nose bleeding, delirium, great loss of flesh, abdominal pain (which may be its typical intestinal perforation) and a red rash. This sounds very like it. Scarlet fever, if it existed, is lost in a nebula of ill-defined symptoms until it emerges as 'rossania' in sixteenth-century Naples. Over the past four hundred years it has fluctuated greatly in severity and it may have been as benign in ancient Greece as it is now in modern England, in sharp contrast to the virulence with which it decimated Victorian nurseries. Another elusive disease is diphtheria. Aretaeus of Cappadocia (second century A.D.), one of the greatest medical writers between Hippocrates and Avicenna, is vivid in his description of tonsils blanketed by a grey slough or membrane that may suffocate the patient if it forms a plug across the windpipe. In persons afflicted with this 'Syriac ulcer' he says that food may slop back through the nostrils; an almost certain sign of diphtheritic paralysis of the soft palate. Little more is definitely known of it until it reappears as 'garotillo' in sixteenth-century Spain.

Of all the infections to which man is exposed none is more dreaded and fraught with panic than plague, a deadly murrain caused by the small organism *Pasteurella pestis*. It can occur in two forms: the bubonic, in which swelling and suppuration of the glands is prominent, and the pneumonic, in which the lungs are attacked. Pneumonic plague is almost always fatal within four days. In spite of the dramatic nature of this disease its early history is hidden in diagnostic obscurity and not until Rufus of Ephesus (*fl.* A.D. 115) do we find an unequivocal account of it. In his time it seems chiefly to have affected Egypt, Libya and Syria but during the sixth century it flowered into an epidemic of appalling virulence which spread through most of Europe, north Africa and hither Asia. This was the Plague of Justinian and we know a great deal about the catastrophe from the description left by Evagrius of Antioch and by Procopius, both of whom lived through these nightmare years. At its peak the death rate soared to heights unknown in any previous epidemic but eventually the toll abated and, strangely, the disease seems to have slumbered unobtrusively for several centuries until, in 1345, it awakened from its torpor to unleash the fury of the Black Death. This time it entered Europe from Caffa in the Crimea, where it had been introduced by a besieging army of Tartars, after which it swept most of the known world in a vast pandemic of horror. Plague is not primarily a human disease. Its natural host is the black rat (*Rattus rattus*) but if many of these rodents are killed in an epizootic the fleas that they harbour and which suck their germ-curdled blood are forced to emigrate and, for want of more attractive lodging, seek asylum on man. The range of the infection is limited therefore by the habitat of the black rat and there is evidence that, although the plague seethed through western Europe to Narbonne, Arles, Clermont and Dijon during the Justinian efflorescence, it never entered Britain because at that time the black rat, like the rabbit, was not native to the islands. After it had been introduced several centuries later by returning Crusaders no lucky chance of ecology stood between the English and the Black Death.

Plate 37

When Neolithic man learnt to domesticate animals and till the land he extended an open invitation to tetanus. Aretaeus, who not only discoursed on pleurisy, epilepsy, jaundice, tuber-culosis and probably leprosy but also first described diabetes and gave it its present name, left a full account of the convul-sions of lockjaw which 'arch the patient's back like a drawn bow and drag his head between his shoulder blades. An in-human calamity! a spectacle agonizing even to the beholder; a malady beyond all cure!' His description dispels any doubt about its identity that we may have from reading the Hip-pocratic records of fatal convulsions after wounds and burns or the even earlier account in the Edwin Smith papyrus of a person whose jaw became stiff and his neck rigid after a gaping wound in the head. Some of the Hippocratic cases might equally well be meningitis, but a good medieval description of a gardener who died of tetanus after cutting his thumb when pruning a vine is given by John Arderne of Newark (1307–80). He tells how the man 'had such spasms of his face and arms that he could get no food past his jaws nor open his mouth and this cramp seized him all the time until after three weeks he died.' Opisthotonos, a tetanoid retraction of the neck muscles due to infection or poisoning, has been described in dinosaurs but the attribution is almost certainly erroneous.

Cholera occupies the curious position of having debouched into epidemiological significance only within the past hundred and fifty years but there are reasons for believing that it may have been endemic in a mild form in India from a far-distant period. A few wisps of evidence tempt the unwary to ascribe it also to ancient China but any real proof of it is lost in a magic-lantern obscurity. Malaria is a disease with such clear-cut symptoms that it is surprising that its early history is not more precisely known. There is indirect evidence that it was widespread throughout the ancient world from remote antiquity and the brilliance of the Hippocratic account makes it unmistakable.

Before this a slim tradition credits Empedocles of Agrigentum (*c.* 490–430 B.C.) with having quelled an epidemic of this fever at Selinos in Sicily by draining the marshes around the town. Enlargement of the spleen is typical of this disease and mummies have been found in which splenic hypertrophy suggests infection by the malarial protozoon. It is also likely that of the specific diseases so far mentioned this was the only one to exist in precolumbian America: the use of cinchona bark by the Incas may be related to its anti-malarial properties.

A perfect thumb-nail sketch of mumps is given by Hippo-crates. He says (*Epidemics I*), 'Many people had swellings close to both ears, usually without fever. . . . Most of these patients were adolescents and young men who thronged the judo school and gymnasia. Few of the women were affected. . . . Tender engorgement in either or both of the testicles was found and then a raised temperature might or might not ensue. Usually they were excruciatingly painful.'

We may now briefly mention a few diseases caused by larger parasites. Bilharzia, due to several species of Schistosoma that use snails as an intermediate host, leads to extensive bleeding from the genito-urinary and intestinal tracts. The disease is one of the scourges of modern Egypt as it must have been in dynastic times. Several mummies have been found with their kidneys infested with the eggs of this trematode. Filariasis is the nema-tode infection that produces some of the forms of elephantiasis. The worms and their embryos block the lymph ducts and this leads to swelling of the glands and other tissues, especially in in the legs and scrotum. It occurs widely in Africa and Asia and representations of it are not uncommon in early tribal art. Another filarial infection is guinea worm (*Dracunculus medi-nensis*). The females, which may be more than two feet in length, descend from the abdomen into the leg where they give rise to a pricking or burning sensation until they can be tied to a small rod of wood and slowly, over many days, wound

Plate 42

out of the tissues through an incision in the skin. Although the evidence is meagre it has been suggested that guinea worms were the fiery serpents which afflicted the Israelites after the Exodus.

So much for the infections that do not attack bone; we must now turn to those which do.

A rare but horrible one is actinomycosis. This is due to the ray fungus and is the cause of the well-known 'woody jaw' in cattle. No indubitable case is known from human palaeopathology but a long history is proposed for this disease by its having been diagnosed in *Aphelops*, a fossil rhinoceros. More important is anterior poliomyelitis or infantile paralysis. This can have a most insidious onset, especially in young children in whom the initial febrile phase may evoke almost no attention until the victim is found to have a paralysed arm or leg which may then be thought to result from the child having been dropped by a careless nursemaid. With this in mind a biblical case has been postulated from II Samuel iv, 4: 'And Jonathan, Saul's son, had a son that was lame of his feet. He was five years old when the tidings came of Saul and Jonathan out of Jezreel, and his nurse took him up, and fled: and it came to pass, as she made haste to flee, that he fell, and became lame. And his name was Mephibosheth.' Possible but doubtful, is the most we can say of this case. In skeletal material it can be recognized by the atrophy or failure to develop of the bones of one or more limbs, as in a neolithic man from Cissbury, Sussex, that was excavated in 1878. The left humerus and radius of this specimen were much shorter and lighter than their fellows of the right side. A closely similar case of Bronze Age date has been found at Barton Bendish, Norfolk, and occasional examples are reported from all continents. It has been diagnosed in an Egyptian mummy from Deshasheh, and Raymond Baby in his careful analysis of cremated material from Hopewell mounds, Ohio, has recognized a club-foot deformity that could perhaps be the result of this disease although he does not claim it as such. Enough evidence survives therefore to make it highly probable that infantile paralysis did exist at an early period but an alternative diagnosis is nearly always possible especially when the assessment depends on a single withered arm. Perhaps the most convincing case is that of the XVIII Dynasty priest Ruma whose shrunken right leg and drawn-up foot could be duplicated today in thousands of living victims of paralytic poliomyelitis.

Plate 44

Leprosy is another disease of uncertain antiquity. The well-known references to it in Classical writers and the Bible are wholly misleading. The λέπρα of the Greeks was a mixture of impetigo, lichen and other skin lesions but never leprosy as we know it today. The 'elephas' and 'elephantiasis' of Celsus and Lucretius probably included true leprosy among a complex of diseases in which psoriasis was also prominent. The same can be said of the Egyptian disease *sebek*. It has the advantage, however, of being quite certainly recognizable when advanced skeletal changes are present though minor degrees of it are often deceptive. Typically the diagnosis rests on an inflammation followed by erosion of the bone in and around the nose, with loss of the upper central teeth and destruction of the small bones of the feet and hands. One of the first cases to be described was in a Byzantine Egyptian of the sixth century A.D., but very few had been recognized until the brilliant exposition by Møller-Christensen of the medieval leper cemetery at Aarderup, Denmark. This was only one among many leprosaria in the country but over two hundred cases were excavated to testify to the prevalence of the disease during the Middle Ages. It is difficult to estimate how common it really was. In England about two hundred leper hospitals existed in the thirteenth century but errors of diagnosis must have been frequent and many unfortunate outcasts were condemned to social death as lepers when in fact they suffered from some quite different

Plate 41

Plate 43

complaint. A skull recovered from the leper ground of St James, Ipswich, illustrates this. It had many holes eroded in it by secondary deposits of a malignant tumour; in life these would have ulcerated through the scalp and were probably assumed to be leprosy. But it must be remembered that, when the rigorous policy of ostracism had at last reduced the number of lepers, the old institutions often continued in use for other types of cases, just as modern tuberculosis sanatoria are now used for mental and general diseases. At the height of its spread in Europe about one person in every two hundred may have been a leper. The first English cases to be identifiable are from the Early Saxon period but it may have been introduced into the country by the Romans.

Plate 50

Until more skeletal evidence is available its original centre must remain uncertain; an Eastern focus is likely and there is little doubt that it spread widely in the Orient during the first millennium A.D. Long before this, however, a good description of the disease can be found in the Sushruta Samhita where its treatment by chaulmoogra oil, still used in the present century, is noted. The existing recension of Sushruta's work was compiled about 600 B.C. but it embodies earlier material and descriptions of what seems to be leprosy are found in the Manu Smriti and the Vedas, where it is called *kushtha*. In the Far East it does not appear in burial grounds until relatively recent times though there are detailed accounts of it in the *Ch'ien Chin Yao Fang* or 'Thousand Gold Remedies' compiled by Sun Szu-mo in the T'ang dynasty (A.D. 619–907) and in other works such as Ch'ao's textbook of pathology (A.D. 610). The measures devised for treating it give some idea of the horror in which it was held; in addition to the usual regimen of purges, diaphoretics and drugs, which included arsenic and chaulmoogra, the sufferer was made to endure snake bites and scorpion stings. In Japan the disease was already widespread by the eighth century A.D. when Komyo, wife of the Emperor

Shomu, founded what may have been the first leper hospital in the country at Nara. When it reached Australia is unknown; it has not been found in central aboriginal groups and it was probably brought only recently by Malay and white infiltration.

Much argument has centred round the problem of whether leprosy occurred in precolumbian America. It has been found neither in Peruvian mummies nor in excavated bones and there are many facts that enable us to reject it with confidence. The theory that it existed in the New World is chiefly based on the facial deformities that are found in the *huacos* or water-jars of Peru, Bolivia and Ecuador. These vases are made in a style of highly naturalistic portraiture. Many show destruction of the lips and nose and this may be combined with loss or deformity of the feet. The appearance is superficially not unlike leprosy but the pots are quite common and enough survive to make it certain that an entirely different disease is intended. This is known by various native names, the commonest of which are *uta* and *espundia*. It is a form of leishmaniasis and therefore related to the Burmese and African kala-azar. In *uta* the soft tissues of the face are the prime target for ulcerative destruction, but a few of the *huacos* may be intended to show not so much the disease itself as surgical amputation of the lips and nose designed to cure it or even, it has been supposed, as a punitive mutilation. A vase of this type has been described in which an operator is shown cutting off the lips of a patient or victim with a broad-bladed *tumis*. There is another possibility: that some of these ceramics represented paracoccidioidomycosis, a disease due to the yeast-like organism *Blastomyces brasiliensis* and one which is at times clinically indistinguishable from *espundia*. Many of the Mochica pots portray these kinds of mutilation and it is interesting to find that amputations of the limbs are quite commonly shown whereas they occur but rarely in the burial grounds. This is another warning that secondary sources of evidence do not always reflect with accuracy what obtained at the time. *Uta*

Plates 45, 46

Plate 49

was almost invariably fatal and its frequent appearance on these vases is no doubt an expression of the terror it inspired.

Huacos, having led by an easy transition from leprosy to *uta*, lead on again to another condition peculiar to Andean America, Oroya fever or verruga peruana, which is caused by *Bartonella bacilliformis*. This highly infectious malady is associated with severe wasting, fever, anaemia and ultimately a crop of fungating warts on the skin. It has a high mortality in the acute phase and has been thought to be the disease chiefly responsible for the collapse of the Aztec empire. On his third and last expedition to Peru in 1531 it attacked Francisco Pizarro's band of ruffians. W. H. Prescott in his *History of the Conquest of Peru* writes: 'To add to their distresses, a strange epidemic broke out in the little army. It took the form of ulcers, or rather hideous warts of great size, which covered the body, and when lanced, as was the case with some, discharged such a quantity of blood as proved fatal to the sufferer. Several died of this frightful disorder, which was so sudden in its attack, and attended with such prostration of strength, that those who lay down well at night were unable to lift their hands to their heads in the morning.' Water-jars showing the rash have been found in early sites and though its importance in the fall of the Aztecs has been exaggerated there is evidence that at one time it extended far to the north of its present territory. A ceremonial mask of the god Quetzalcoatl probably shows this disease.

Plate 47

Plate 48

Before the New World was raped by the Old its inhabitants enjoyed a high level of health. We have already seen that smallpox, typhus, diphtheria, plague and cholera were absent. Malaria may have existed before the Spanish invasion but it is likely that yellow fever, later to be a killer of millions, had hardly emerged from its natural reservoir in the blood stream of Amazonian capuchin monkeys. These animals, who haunt the high canopy of the tropical forests and rarely descend to ground level, resist the organism they carry whereas the black howler monkey rapidly succumbs. In the recent northward extension of the disease it was the silence falling on the forest as the stricken howlers died that warned the villagers to flee its approach. But before we can assert that the native Americans were remarkably free from infection their status in relation to two more diseases must be considered: tuberculosis and syphilis.

Tuberculosis has certain features that make it especially interesting to the palaeopathologist. Firstly, it can occur in many animals besides man. There is a strain of it which is common in cattle and this suggests that it might have an antiquity independent of its human associations. Secondly, although its soft-tissue manifestations are neatly characterized the skeletal lesions are usually ambiguous. Several neolithic specimens have been labelled tubercular. In 1907 Bartels described one from Heidelberg in which the thoracic vertebrae had collapsed and telescoped in a typically tubercular fashion. Although the case has become classic, in it looms the dilemma posed by this infection because several leading medical historians cast doubt on the diagnosis and some have thought that the Heidelberg spine was traumatic in origin despite its intact vertebral arches. Even if this case is rejected, likely examples of tuberculosis have been tagged for the Neolithic period in the Grenelle hip joint from Paris, a spine from Dakka, Egypt, an ankle from l'Aumède, Lozère and many others. It must be admitted that almost any of these could equally be due to staphylococcal or similar non-specific infections, yet the cumulative evidence is impressive and we can be sure that tuberculosis did flourish at an early date because a perfect case survives in an Egyptian mummy of the XXI Dynasty. This was a priest of Amen in whom a vertebral infection had tunnelled under the sheath of the psoas muscle to produce, low down in the abdomen, an abscess of a kind peculiar to this disease. Tuberculosis has also been identified in the lungs of a Byzantine mummy and at least a dozen other convincing cases are known from predynastic and dynastic times in which it is localized in the spine. This evidence of Pott's disease (it is named after Percival Pott, the eponym of the leg fracture) is reinforced in Egypt by figurines of hunchbacks which suggest that the infection was fairly common there. It is likely that much of the human disease came from drinking the milk of infected cattle; illustrations of these animals sometimes hint that they were severely ill and in a bas-relief from Mer (XII Dynasty) the emaciated figure of the herdsman himself, whose ribs stand out like the struts of a toast-rack as he leans in weariness upon his staff, might well be that of a man in the advanced stages of consumption.

Although some of the Neolithic or Bronze Age examples from many different European and Near Eastern sites are unconvincing, there is no reason to reject them all or to doubt the early appearance of the disease even if in some areas it was late to arrive. It is unconfirmed before the twelfth century A.D. in Scandinavia where two cases of calcification of the pleura attest to the presence of consumptives among the medieval group at Aebelholt. The clinical manifestations of the disease are far from constant even today and they seem to have been just as variable in antiquity. Although a virulent and rapidly fatal form was described by Hippocrates, it is uncertain how widely spread tuberculosis was in the classical world: it seems to have been common. Further confirmation of this is obtained from statuettes. An ivory carving of a negro is almost certainly meant to show Pott's disease and a terracotta from Myrina portrays a hunchback in which a psoas abscess has tracked all the way from the spine to the groin, a well-known clinical event and one which greatly reduces the element of doubt in the diagnosis. A unique document, dating from about the first century A.D., is a sepulchral inscription from Smyrna. It is the epitaph of a four-year-old child, L. Minikios Anthimianos, and is contrived in the form of a quasi-autobiographical case history: 'A helpless child am I within this tomb, O wayfarer . . .' It des-

Plate 51

Plate 52

Plate 53

cribes how his father, apparently a physician, treated him for a swelling of the testicles which eventually subsided only to be followed by necrosis of the bones in his left foot. These were scraped away by his father's friends, but soon his body began to waste whilst his belly swelled huge with fluid until he died. This is typical of the disease, the final phase being a tuberculous peritonitis.

In India early Hindu texts describe the infection in domesticated elephants and it certainly affected people, too. It is established for medieval eastern Asia by no less a person than Tamerlaine (1336–1405), whose name simply means Timur the Lame. When the Gur Amir mausoleum in Samarkand was opened the interred remains were identified as Timur's by the extensive tuberculous cavitation of his right thigh and shin bones, and by the bony union that had immobilized his knee joint, and his right arm. These findings confirmed the literary records which describe him as walking with a limp and having a stiff right arm. Contrary to some traditions he was not an albino: remains of a grey-grizzled dark-chestnut beard survived. The evidence for China and the Far East is inconclusive, but an extremely common result of female foot-binding in the past two or three centuries has been tuberculous infection of the tarsal bones, much like that which attacked little Anthimianos of Smyrna. It is possible that the Australian aborigines were free of it until white infiltration began: the same can be said of South Africa.

Plates 54, 55

Plate 56

The problem of the presence of tuberculosis in precolumbian America is peculiarly interesting. Twenty-five years ago Moodie and Hrdlička, whose combined experience of New World palaeopathology was unrivalled, were not convinced that it existed there before 1492. Since then many cases have been put forward by different workers to support a diagnosis of tuberculosis before the Conquest. It has even been suggested that a pelvic lesion in a sabre-tooth tiger (*Smilodon californicus*) from

La Brea was tubercular. More convincing examples have been diagnosed in Ohio Mound Builders, Pueblo dwellers, early Maya groups and ancient Peruvians, among whom hunch-backed mummies have been found. Lupus vulgaris is a tuber-culous infection of the skin and soft tissues which destroys the nose and other parts of the face. It has been surmised that the anthropomorphic Peruvian water-pots with facial mutilation are meant to show lupus. There is little to support this view: as already stated, the disease portrayed is *uta* and if tuberculosis of the skin ever occurred no signs of it have survived. There is

Plate 57

a strong case for diagnosing tuberculosis in the precolumbian Iroquois. As well as skeletal evidence a Cayuga pottery pipe has been found in the shape of a kyphotic (hunchbacked) figurine showing the pigeon breast, wasting and facial expression typical of Pott's disease. From San Domingo in the West Indies we

Plate 58

have an aboriginal grain-pounder in the shape of a humpback. On the strength of all this evidence it has been said that the

Plate 59

presence of the disease in pre-conquest America, north and south, must be accepted as definite. Against this, Morse, after a cautious review of the skeletal and artistic sources, has recently claimed that not a single case is sufficiently clear-cut to sustain the diagnosis: he therefore rejects it for the New World whilst accepting it for the Old.

Plates 60, 61

The last major infection to be discussed is syphilis and it confronts us with one of the most puzzling enigmas in the history of disease: did it occur in either the Old World or the New before Columbus returned from America? And if so, in which? Two main theories contest the field and they are mutually exclusive. One holds that syphilis had existed for many centuries in Europe, having originally evolved in Palaeo-lithic times, perhaps in Africa or the Near East, and that it only reached America when the Spaniards took it there. The evidence to support this view is a pastiche of facts that emerge with the tenuity of a grisaille rather than the boldness of chiaroscuro. The second theory asserts that it was an American disease wholly unknown in the Old World until Columbus and his infected crew brought it back from Haiti to Portugal and Spain in March 1493 at the end of his first voyage. Thereafter it attacked an unprotected population with devastating effect and rapidity, being taken by Spaniards in the army of King Charles of France to the siege of Naples, whence it was at once disseminated by home-wending soldiers throughout the continent. It was called, according to the partiality of the observer, either the Neapolitan disease or the morbus gallicus.

An early exponent of this view was Oviedo, the first historian of the Americas. He says: 'Many times in Italy did I laugh when the Italians named it the French disease whilst the French called it the disease of Naples. Both sides would have uttered truth had they called it the malady of the Indies.' Oviedo's laughter has grown historic and its echoes still mock the wrangling of medical historians. Further support for this view of syphilis comes from Diaz de Isla who published his *Tractado contra el mal serpentino* in 1539 and in it describes the same disease under the arabesque of a new name, whilst claiming to have seen twenty thousand cases of it. He is emphatic that it was unknown before the return of Columbus. Both these writers have an air of reliability about them and the beguiling simplicity of their theory, combined with its dramatic appeal and a certain psychological piquancy, has ensured its popularity.

There are, of course, other possibilities but they have had few advocates. Syphilis might have emerged as a new European disease in 1493 by a hitherto harmless organism mutating to become pathogenic. (The treponeme which causes it belongs to a widely distributed group.) Or it might have existed as a relatively benign condition in both hemispheres from an early period, flaring into virulence at the end of the fifteenth century for unknown reasons that had nothing to do with Columbus.

The emotional aura surrounding this interesting infection is, even today, far from dispelled and protagonists of the opposing theories still attack, with curiously unscientific passion and acrimony, those whose opinions differ from their own. The evidence, though puzzling, hardly justifies the virulence with which it is propounded. Here we can do no more than distil the essence from a few of the conflicting views: the following are some of the arguments put forward by those who reject the theory of its Columbian origin.

Despite the clear statements of Oviedo and de Isla a close scrutiny of their writings reveals that both authors, and especially the latter, are bad witnesses. De Isla is ambiguous and contradicts himself. He says his serpentine disease first appeared in Barcelona but adds that it was the same as the lichen of the Greeks and the kiss-spread mentagra of Pliny. Moreover, contemporary opinion was divided: Angelus Blondus in his 1542 *De origine morbi gallici* refutes the notion that it was an import from America. It is suggested that the disease had long been known in Europe and that many precolumbian references to it can be found but they are masked under the name of 'lepra'. The evidence here is strong. Bernadus de Gordonio in 1303 stresses four outstanding facts about lepra: that it was highly contagious, that it was acquired venereally, that its incubation period was short and that children were often born with it. All these statements fit syphilis; none is true of leprosy. This characteristic quartet of the infectious, venereal, quickly developing and congenital nature of 'lepra' is regularly met in early medical literature. It is found in the works of Joannes Platearius (fl. eleventh century), in John of Gaddesden (1280–1361), in Arnold of Villanova (1235–1312) and in Henry of Mondeville (*fl.* 1306–20). In the *Cyrurgia* of Theodoric (1205–96) the following passage occurs: 'Item, potest generari ex coitu leprosi cum pregnante; quia inficitur foetus; licet non inficitur mater.' This is typical of syphilis and quite unlike leprosy.

The teaching of these men made less impact than might have been expected because they were overshadowed by Guy de Chauliac (1300–68) who, from his eminence as physician to three Popes, exerted immense influence whilst basing his theories of disease on an out-of-date humoral philosophy which largely ignored external infection. Enough remains, however, to make it apparent that although the precolumbian lepra no doubt embraced cases of true leprosy, it also, through diagnostic imprecision, included the identical post-columbian malady of morbus gallicus, lues venerea or syphilis. To accept a Columbian origin for the disease commits us to a belief that less than fifty sailors were a sufficient nucleus to infect the continent of Europe within eighteen months. Many critics feel that this conflicts too violently with epidemiological probability and they seek evidence of European epidemics before 1493. At least one such visitation, in 1484, certainly looks very like a sharp efflorescence of the disease. A further point in favour of precolumbian syphilis is the high regard in which mercury was held in ancient and medieval times. The 'Saracens' ointment', so popular with the Crusaders for treating 'lepra', was quick-silver in a fatty base. Inert against true leprosy, it is a specific for the treponemal infections. Inunctions of cinnabar (mercuric sulphide) are still used by Arab apothecaries, and ancient Chinese texts also speak of the efficacy of this drug. The problem of syphilis is complicated by the fact that many millions of people have the disease in what is known as the endemic or non-venereal form (the Arabic *bejel*). This is usually acquired in early childhood from other infected children who may pass it on to any adult who has hitherto escaped contagion. The treponemes which produce both forms of syphilis and also yaws and the American disease pinta are all morphologically indistinguishable, and despite slight serological differences between them some very experienced syphilologists adopt a unitarian view and regard all four diseases as different environ-

Plate 62

mental responses to a single treponematosis. Cross-immunity between the four conditions is well established and lends weight to this opinion; there is even some evidence that in fluctuating environments one disease can change into another. Recently C. J. Hackett, in a lucid analysis of the problem, has suggested that pinta evolved as the first Old World treponeme infection in Palaeolithic times and that it changed by successive muta-tions of the organism into yaws, endemic syphilis (trepenarid) and venereal syphilis.

Finally, there is the skeletal evidence. The fact that Elliot Smith and Wood Jones found no syphilis in many thousands of Egyptian mummies has been used to rebut the theory of its

Plate 66

African or Asiatic origin. On the other hand Moodie and Hrdlička claimed that the characteristic lesions of the disease had never been found in pre-conquest Amerindians. Both these views have been challenged and many bones with a damascene of 'snail-track' ulcers have been diagnosed as syphi-litic from sites as far apart as precolumbian Paracas, Bronze Age trans-Baikalia, Neolithic France and San Cristobal Pueblo, New Mexico. But at least some of the specimens admit of several interpretations and might equally be due to non-specific infections. Adachi recognizes the condition in the leg bones of a shell-mound burial at Katouhita, Japan, but Dohi doubts both the diagnosis and the age of the deposit. He thinks the Far East was unaffected by syphilis until the Portu-guese took it there, although its presence in China has been claimed as early as 2000 B.C. Several Egyptian cases have been put forward but in some of them the appearance of the bone was due to the post-mortem activities of beetles. There is strong evidence that the Pacific Islands were free from syphilis until recent centuries and a suspicious group of lesions in a Mariana child is much more likely to be yaws in view of its carbon-14 dating to the ninth century A.D. In one form of syphilis, as also in yaws, juxta-articular swellings are common; a painted wooden figure from the Sepik River, New Guinea, shows what could be a faithful representation of such nodules. These few examples give some idea of the conflict of opinion and real difficulty of decision where syphilis is concerned. But despite all statements to the contrary there remains a small number of bones from widely scattered American sites (Ohio mounds; Rio Negro, Argentina; Canete, Peru; Tlaltelolco, Mexico) that are extremely difficult to explain by any other diagnosis. Even so, the evidence of precolumbian specimens from the Old World is hardly less strong and it may be that, until a serological test is available to abate all doubt, the balance of evidence tilts to the view that syphilis is an infection of hoary antiquity on both sides of the Atlantic.

We can now epitomize this sketchy panorama of the specific infections. Many of our current diseases can be traced back through medieval to early historic times until the vagueness of the records baffles diagnosis. In most places and periods measures of public health or hygiene have had a negligible effect on the march of epidemics; the ruthless sanctions against leprosy were an exception to this and during the Middle Ages quarantine edicts increasingly modified the onslaught of a handful of other pestilences. In the prehistoric era and, above all, before the start of neolithic town dwelling it is likely that many ailments which later rose to epidemic levels rarely or never occurred. Medical texts give strong support for the existence of malaria, smallpox, typhus, typhoid and leprosy in the first millennium B.C., as they do for tetanus and infective jaundice. Plague, scarlet fever and diphtheria are less certain, cholera extremely doubtful, and yellow fever definitely late in asserting itself and always limited by the natural habitat of its insect vectors, the *Aëdes* and *Haemogogus* mosquitoes. Tuberculosis is perhaps the oldest of the specific infections that can be diagnosed. It is described in the Hippocratic corpus and seems identifiable from bones at least as far back as the Neolithic

Age; we cannot readily estimate its antiquity in the Americas but it almost certainly ante-dates the Conquest. Syphilis probably adorned both hemispheres before the Columbian expedition, but the evidence still falls short of absolute proof.

ENDOCRINE AND METABOLIC DISORDERS

There were giants in the earth in those days.
GENESIS IV, 4

Endocrine diseases are due to abnormal activity of the ductless glands, usually a qualitative chemical change in the hormones they secrete. This perverts the behaviour of the body with far-reaching effects on the metabolism of many different tissues. Endocrine diseases are, therefore, metabolic diseases but in practice this latter term is more often reserved for conditions in which the deviant chemical processes arise, so far as we know, from sources other than the ductless glands. Evidence that these conditions existed in early times is elusive.

Diabetes, a dysfunction of the islets of Langerhans in the pancreas, may be a disease of great antiquity. Before insulin was available to treat it gangrene, especially of the feet, was a common terminal event and whenever skeletal remains are found with septic osteitis and destruction of bone, diabetes ranks high among the possible diagnoses. But deprived of the clinical history, as we always are in prehistoric material, there is no certain way of discriminating between this condition and other forms of osteitis and gangrene such as frost-bite, ergotism, senile arteriosclerosis and much else. It is not until the second century A.D. that doubt is removed in a graphic description of the disease by Aretaeus of Cappadocia. He says:

Diabetes is an astonishing affection... being a melting down of the flesh ... into urine ... The patients never stop making water . . . The flow is incessant like the opening of aqueducts . . . It is a chronic disease but the patient is short-lived . . . and his thirst unquenchable.

Thereafter it was well recognized, and the profuse leakage of sugar into the sufferer's urine was easily detectable when it cloyed sweetly diagnostic on the tongues of alert medieval physicians just as it had centuries earlier on the lips of Sushruta the Indian.

Dysfunction of the pituitary gland can produce many different abnormalities some of which imprint themselves on the skeleton. The most obvious is gigantism in which the growth-promoting hormone is over-active and individuals far taller than the average are produced. The folklore of most peoples enshrines tales of giants who anciently tramped the earth, and until recent times biblical authority for this belief was accepted throughout Christendom. At the end of the eighteenth century the Abbé Henrion deduced with mathematical solemnity that Adam was a hundred and thirty feet tall, Abraham thirty but Moses a mere thirteen. In fact the limit of human gigantism seems to be somewhere about eight and a half feet. Skeletons that fall well short of this can cause perplexity as did an extremely tall Saxon from Burgh Castle, Norfolk. He stood about 7 ft. 4 in. and we may wonder whether this is truly a case of endocrine gigantism or whether he was merely the last man on the Gaussian curve of normal variation of stature for his group. Pituitary giants sometimes have bones that are pathologically fragile and this Saxon had severe fractures of his right humerus, both ulnae and his right tibia, whilst his right ankle and heel bones were fused together as a result of each having been broken: a cadence of injuries which greatly adds to the likelihood that this was a real pituitary dysfunction.

The concept of *racial* gigantism has been put forward to explain evolutionary trends. On this theory the luxuriant

growth and eventual extinction of such creatures as the plesiosaurs and diplodocus is attributed to abnormal glandular
activity. Applied to man, it has been surmised that hormonal
change of this kind explains the tall stature and ultimate disappearance of the Cro-Magnon Upper Palaeolithic people
and that the Shilluks of the Sudan are victims of a similar
process today. At present it is impossible to pass a final judgement on this theory: it may contain facets which reflect some
image of the truth.

Another pituitary disease is acromegaly. In this condition,
which is progressive during adult life, the hands and feet en-
large and a highly characteristic change appears in the face with
excessive growth of the lower jaw and thickening of the nose
and supra-orbital ridges. A few cases have been identified,
almost all on insecure evidence, from neolithic cemeteries in
Switzerland, pre-white Australia and Patagonia. It is sometimes said that the portrait coins of Maximinus (A.D. 235–
238), who is known to have been a man of great stature, show
him as suffering from this disease, and it is strongly suggested
by a fifteenth-century Benin bronze head; but perhaps the most
convincing early example, although of an unusual type, is the
Egyptian king Akhenaten (c. 1365 B.C.). Much argument has
swirled round this remarkable man but some of the statues
and certain anatomical details of his skull make it extremely
difficult to reject an acromegalic element in his strange appearance. The fact that his hands and feet were normal rules out a
simple acromegaly and it may be that this dark riddle in diagnosis is best resolved by supposing that he had a pituitary
tumour of the kind known as a chromophobe adenoma.

Another important ductless gland is the thyroid. Broadly
speaking it can be said that in children under-activity of the
organ produces cretinism whereas in adults myxoedema, with
loss of hair, dry skin and sluggish behaviour, is the result. Its
over-activity leads to Graves' disease (toxic or exophthalmic

Plate 68

goitre). Only in the stunted growth of cretins do we find skeletal changes and a few cases have been diagnosed in scat-tered burial grounds throughout the world, whilst further evidence of its antiquity is given by its portrayal in Tanagra terracottas. The full neck, protruding eyes and tense expression of toxic goitre is occasionally seen in early art. A figurine from Veii is a good example and it is, perhaps, recognizable in a Mochica vase. Much later, Leonardo da Vinci used a case as a model for one of his drawings. The huge non-toxic or en-demic goitre of mountain regions was well known to classical writers and a good account of it is given by the Elder Pliny.

Plate 63

Metabolic diseases other than those of endocrine origin need not long detain us. Gout is one and a perfect example of it survives from an early Christian cemetery on the island of Philae in the Nile. It is the mummy of an old man, with long hair and flowing white beard, whose joints were packed with large concretions of a chalky substance that on analysis gave the chemical reactions of uric acid. His air of benign calm is un-likely to be a reflection of his true personality: peevish irrita-bility is the hall-mark of this disease. The exact cause of gout is still unknown. That it should puzzle the physicians of the ancient world is not surprising and we can sympathize with Aretaeus and even share his exasperation when he grumbles that only the gods can make head or tail of it.

The minor deviations of metabolic activity which lead to obesity have a long history. We cannot tell how fat the Neandertals could become but many Egyptian mummies survive to confirm the evidence of statues and bas-reliefs that plumpness was not unusual, and persons cast in a Falstaffian mould appear in early Greek and Roman pottery. A Boeotian terracotta of a massive, blowzy woman closely resembles Cushing's syndrome, a disease due to hyperfunction of the adrenal glands, in which breasts, belly and buttocks roll with excessive fat and the face swells to a moon-like vacuity. But

Plate 65

Plate 64

this statuette could represent nothing more than a metabolic middle-age spread, being intended, perhaps, to portray a gone-to-seed courtesan; similar figures in doubtfully alluring postures are not uncommon. The squat and podgy gods or sages found in Chinese porcelain are more often artistic conventions than true representations of adiposity, but Hippocrates forestalled modern life insurance actuaries with his statement that corpulent persons die more quickly than slim ones.

One of the strangest metabolic diseases is alkaptonuria or ochronosis. It could equally well be discussed in company with the congenital abnormalities for it is due to an inborn genetic error. It reveals itself with dramatic simplicity, the urine turning dark brown or black shortly after it has been voided. This physiological freak is extremely rare; in western Europe and the United States a frequency of one in ten million has been estimated. The startling appearance of the urine ensures that it will be noticed in early infancy but the child thrives normally and only when adult life is reached are further changes discovered. The homogentisic acid responsible for the urinary pigmentation gradually leads to modifications in the intervertebral discs of the spine. The cartilage becomes brittle and more dense and shows in a radiograph as opaque white bands. No other condition looks in the least like it and its recent discovery in an Egyptian mummy of the Roman period was a remarkable event. To check on the diagnosis, in view of its rarity, it was decided to radiograph further examples. The very

Plate 69   first to be done revealed another perfect case of the disease. This can only mean that owing to inbreeding or some unknown cause alkaptonuria must have been much more common in ancient Egypt than it is either there or in the western world today, since there is nothing to suggest that the appearance of the discs is a result of the embalming process.

One more metabolic disease, also a genetic anomaly, may be mentioned—favism. This condition is due to deficiency of glucose-6-phosphate dehydrogenase, an enzyme of red blood cells, and in susceptible persons leads to a dangerous, often fatal, haemolytic anaemia after eating a diet rich in beans. It is especially common today among Ghanians, Congolese and Thais and also in the eastern Mediterranean area, and is allied to the anaemias which can be a catastrophic sequel of modern medical treatment with chloromycetin or similar drugs. Many details of Pythagorean practice remain veiled in the obscurity common to all mystery cults but we know that it imposed a taboo on the eating of beans. It is likely that Pythagoras (*c.* 550–500 B.C.) or one of his early disciples had already detected this physiological hazard two and a half millennia before its rediscovery in the mid twentieth century and established the prohibition to protect his followers from the disease.

POISONS

Some poison'd by their wives, some sleeping kill'd.

WILLIAM SHAKESPEARE

The long road of palaeopathology is littered with the cadavers of men, women and children who have been battered or sliced or strangled to death. The muster remains unreckoned but it runs into thousands. Yet it may be supposed that every age has thrown up a few rare spirits whose delicately squeamish cast of mind has recoiled from the clumsy violence of the bludgeon, preferring to delete an enemy with a sop of henbane in the goblet of friendship or aconite in a consecrated wafer. Palaeotoxicology thus falls within the ambit of our study. Unfortunately the evidence from early periods is meagre and indecisive, though Nicander had already written an elaborate work on toxicology in the second century B.C. and Aretaeus tells us that some people fancied the plague of Athens was due to poison which the Peloponnesians had slipped into the wells.

Mineral poisons can long persist in the tissues and are easy to identify: heavy concentrations of arsenic have recently been found in a sample of Napoleon's hair. But with this substance and also with lead and other metals it may be difficult to exclude contamination from the soil as being the source of origin, even when they are present in lethal quantity. Sometimes, as with antimony and mercury, their presence implies no sinister motive; it merely reflects their medical popularity in earlier times. Many of the extensive bone lesions in seventeeth- to nineteenth-century syphilitic burials have the appearance of being partly due to heavy metal poisoning and it is a fact that skulls with 'syphilitic' necrosis have been found to contain mercury.

Accidental, sometimes fatal, fluorine poisoning is still common in the Punjab, India. It is due to the high concentration of the mineral in the water, which may reach fourteen parts per million. In severe cases the bones exhibit crippling deformities, are more than twice their normal weight and are permeated or festooned with magnesium fluoride. The condition is unmistakable and has been identified in ancient skeletons from a wide area of the Punjab. An appearance of fluorosis in radiographs of Bronze Age inhumations from the English chalk downs is illusory; it is an example of pseudopathology due to post-mortem physico-chemical changes. A rare congenital abnormality—Kinneir Wilson's disease—inhibits the excretion of the minute amounts of copper which are normally ingested. Eventually the accumulated metal causes fatal damage to the brain and liver. It has not been recognized in early burials but its mention here may serve to indicate the variety of agents that can induce toxic lesions in man and which the palaeopathologist must always be heedful to consider.

Organic poisons are much more labile and elusive than the metals; often their presence can only be inferred. Opisthotonos is a condition in which the body is arched backward by violent spasms of the dorsal muscles. It is characteristic of death from strychnine and from tetanus. R. L. Moodie thought that he recognized it in the fossil of a Cretaceous dinosaur (*Struth/iomimus altus*) from the Red Deer River, Alberta, as well as in other species and that it represented a spastic distress brought on by poisoning of the central nervous system either from infection or from eating toxic substances. Pausing only to mutter the first syllable of this creature's name, a sceptic might wonder how the death spasm was maintained during the putrescence and softening that came after it. The flung/back posture, like a wind/filled spinnaker, in which these long/necked, long/tailed denizens of the past came to rest is much more likely to be due to post/mortem limpness than ante/mortem rigidity and the diagnosis should be expunged from the records. It is certain that no human case has survived from antiquity and apart from fluorosis there is no evidence to warrant a firm assertion of any kind of poisoning until literary sources remove all uncertainty. When once textual evidence appears it leaves no doubt that proficiency in the poisoner's art was indispensable to the education of aspiring statesmen or emperors in the classical period.

An oblique hint, nothing more, may be gathered from a discovery made at Lehringen, Germany, where an elephant (*Elephas antiquus*) was found with a fire/hardened spear of yew wood between two of its ribs. This spear was two and a quarter metres long and of a type adapted for thrusting rather than throwing. It is possible that in order to kill the animal the weapon would have needed to be tipped with a paralysing bane. If any reliance can be placed on this conjecture we can be sure that men, too, must have fallen victims of poisoned lances or arrowheads. The occasional discovery of bodies with a flint point embedded in some non/vital region, yet with no trace of healing in the surrounding bone, would at least be compatible with this suggestion, though hardly proof of it.

DISEASES OF UNKNOWN ORIGIN

Riddles of death Thebes never knew.

P. B. SHELLEY

Plate 70

There are still many diseases of doubtful or unknown origin; several are fairly common in early cemeteries. In cribra orbitalia tiny pits develop in the roof of the eye-socket. It is most frequent in children's skulls and has been thought to be the result of an unidentified deficiency disease but another theory attributes it to a generalized infection of the eye (panophthalmia) leading to blindness. Though its distribution is world-wide it varies greatly in frequency. In one series from ancient Egypt, where blindness was certainly common, it occurred in three-quarters of the skulls but it is unsafe to relate this to the bacteria that have been found in the eyes of mummies as these were more likely to be the organisms of post-mortem putrefaction. Among Anglo-Saxons, cribra was found in only six per cent of two hundred skulls. A similar condition is found, though more rarely, on the frontal and parietal bones. Blindness is always a misfortune; in many societies it is a catastrophe and whether or not associated with cribra its deep impact on human

Plate 72

emotions finds wistful expression in works of art. It is fortunate for the blind when the social structure of their community provides a niche where they can still lead useful lives. In dynastic Egypt, as elsewhere, blind singers and musicians stare with milk-opaque eyes from the murals, wearing their

Plate 6

disability with grace and poise if not contempt. Where no such status is open to them the sightless are apt to fill the role of

Plate 73

communal butt and object of ridicule.

Paget's disease or osteitis deformans is a condition which develops in elderly persons. It affects the head, spine and long bones and causes central rarefaction combined with new bone formation beneath the periosteum, so that thickening occurs. It has been recognized in a French neolithic burial from Lozère and in several other Old World cemeteries. In America it appears in precolumbian mounds near Lynxville, Crawford County, Wisconsin, and at a number of other sites. It is a relatively rare disease today and seems to have been equally so in antiquity.

A few conditions are confined to closely restricted areas. One of these is Kachine-Beck disease, a polyarticular arthrosis that begins in childhood and runs a protracted course. It is common in the inhabitants of the Urow valley, U.S.S.R., and is often said to be due to drinking the water of that river but recent excavations have revealed its presence in medieval and pre-Christian sites far beyond the range of its present distribution. Its social or geographical significance still remains obscure. A remarkable distortion of the lower limb bones is 'boomerang leg'. It occurs in pre-white Australian cemeteries and in tropical Africa. Traditionally it is always ascribed to yaws (framboesia) but recent work makes this doubtful.

Plate 76

These few randomly selected ailments must serve as token representatives of the numerous diseases which turn up as occasional oddities wherever burials are disinterred. Their disparate nature and the uncertainty that shrouds their aetiology make it a ticklish problem to estimate their significance when they appear.

DEFICIENCY DISEASES

I sigh the lack of many a thing I sought.

WILLIAM SHAKESPEARE

The best-known deficiency diseases are due to shortage of vitamins. Although in all severe cases the clinical picture is flamboyant, lack of different vitamins produces totally distinct conditions that lead to very different effects on bone. Scurvy, from insufficient ascorbic acid (C), and rickets, due to shortage of calciferol (D), both produce extensive skeletal changes whereas vitamin A starvation may show itself in little more than mild night blindness when there is not enough to regenerate the visual purple molecule in the retina.

Few diseases have a more interesting history than rickets and few point more clearly to the environmental and social back-ground from which they spring. It is pre-eminently a disease of the twilight, the perpetual twilight of dark tenements in city slums. As long as human beings huddle in ill-ventilated base-ments where rag-hung, grime-crusted windows keep out what-ever light drips through the smoke-laden murk of factory chimneys far above them, there, inevitably, rickets will be found. It is a disease of infants and children and its cauldron is the teeming soot-choked city of the industrial revolution. Only in the last two generations have changing social customs and the advance of medical science slaked its onslaught from the high peak of the nineteenth century until it is now on the way to join such other dead diseases as the green sickness (chlorosis), the dancing mania (tarantism) and 'the vapours'. It must not be thought, however, that rickets was unknown before the industrial revolution. The congested alleys of medie-val towns, cowled by overhanging eaves, were almost as gloomy as Victorian Manchester and the absence of sunlight is, of course, only one element in its onset. Sunshine converts ergo-sterol into vitamin D by irradiation in the skin but diet also plays a basic part in the process either by supplying ready-made viosterol or by providing substances from which it can be synthesized.

The most ancient evidence of rickets is ambiguous. Animals succumb to it as well as man and one of the earliest possible examples comes from the La Brea asphalt pits, California, where a strongly bowed femur of a Pleistocene wolf hints at this disease. Its occurrence under such conditions is quite exceptional and prohibits an easy acceptance of the diagnosis, although a small hawk with an unusually curved long bone was also found at the same site. If any reliance can be placed on these two cases, they may reflect some unique local factor conducive to rickets. More convincing, though still dubious, are the bones of cave bears from Belgium but the first animals to show it unmistakably are Egyptian captive baboons from dynastic tombs in the valley of Gabanet el Giroud.

In human pathology the disease was a rarity everywhere and at all times in prehistoric and early historic periods. When they were first discovered the Java ape/man, the Neandertals and the Cro/Magnons were all thought to be abnormal, and rickets as well as syphilis was invoked to account for them. There is nothing to bolster either diagnosis. Equally clumsy is the attempt to explain the portrait representations of Akhenaten and his family as the result of vitamin D deficiency: constant sunshine in the Nile valley combined with the dietary habits of the people was powerfully prophylactic and throughout the long corridor of Egyptian history human cases were extremely rare. Under the sombre skies of higher latitudes, where a swaddle of clothing muffled out the light, we should expect it to be more lavish. It was scarce at first but from the Neolithic period onwards a trickle of cases seeps out of Norway, Sweden and Denmark until with the late Middle Ages the disease becomes plentiful, at least in cities, across all northern and central Europe. In Hungary a severe degree of it is already found by Roman times at Fazekasboda, and true to its urban character it was common in Rome itself according to Soranus of Ephesus (*fl.* A.D. 117) who gives the first recognizable account of the disease. Its steady increase during the Middle Ages is well shown at Zalavár (Hungary) where it became three times as common in the twelfth century as it had been in the ninth. Outside Europe little early evidence of it can be found. Siamese, Patagonian, and a few other cases are known but most of America, Africa, Australia and Oceania was free of the disease. An adult form of it, osteomalacia, in which

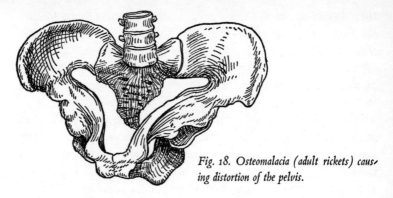

Fig. 18. Osteomalacia (adult rickets) caus~ ing distortion of the pelvis.

Fig. 18

profuse loss of calcium makes the bones as soft as licorice leads to collapse and twisting of the affected parts, especially the pelvis. In recent decades it has been common in China and in Pakistani women who remain in purdah, but it has also been diagnosed in Pleistocene bears and in an early Peruvian.

Plate 71

Scurvy develops in the absence of vitamin C. Ulceration and infection of the gums with loose and falling teeth are prominent signs: many of the edentulous jaws, gross with osteitis of the alveolus, that are found in medieval cemeteries are examples of this condition. It stems from a diet short of fresh fruit or green vegetables and often developed in northern towns during winter and spring. Even rural populations suffered; although enough herbage to prevent the disease grew within easy reach, ignorance of its cause and cure bound the peasants to its ravages. Peoples of the Mediterranean littoral who pickled olives or dried grapes, apricots and other fruit, show little sign of it unless its appearance was triggered by abnormal events, but from the dawn of history until the present century it has been an occupational disease of besieged garrisons and beleagured cities. It rotted the troops of Christina of Denmark when they were invested in Stockholm by the Swedish army (1502) and also an ancient garrison who left their bones in an isolated fortlet in the desert of Sinai beside the Gulf of Akaba, but at the siege of Kut (1916) the Muslim regiments soaked their peas and beans in water for a day or two and by thus eating germinated seeds protected themselves against it. Its constant association with the hard tack and bully of long sea voyages is well known but it is doubtful to what extent it affected short, coast-hugging hauls before the Middle Ages. Another effect of scurvy is to produce clots of blood—haematomata—around the long bones, and the calcified re-mains of these bleedings are common in burial grounds where shed teeth and spongy gums point to a high incidence of the disease.

Plate 77

When vitamin A is deficient resistance to infection slumps. This is often manifested by respiratory ailments, crops of boils, styes on the eyelids and other staphylococcal imbroglios. Night blindness is chemically linked with lack of this substance. None of these conditions is detectable in bone but early evidence of this avitaminosis can be found in the Ebers papyrus where impaired night vision is mentioned and, what is more remark-able, ox liver, a rich source of vitamin A, is prescribed to treat it. The Assyrian medical tract *Sin-lurmâ* also discusses it but counsels a treatment which included antimony, honey and harlot's milk. Provided the last ingredient was copiously avail-able the cure should have been rapid.

The B group of vitamins is an important complex; shortage of its various components leads to severe general and specific illness with beri-beri and pellagra predominating. Here again skeletal evidence is absent but the outstanding impact of beri-beri has for many centuries been on the rice-eating populations of China and many accounts of it occur in early medical texts. The first of these is in the *Nei Ching* or 'Internal Classic', the great Canon of Medicine which is one of the oldest and most important of Chinese medical writings. The existing recension dates from the third century B.C. but it incorporates much earlier material. It contains many references to beri-beri and the disease is repeatedly mentioned in later documents. When Hou Ching besieged the city of Tai in A.D. 501, nine-tenths of the inhabitants are said to have died of it. Ch'ao Yuan-fang gives an accurate clinical description of it in his manual of pathology (A.D. 610); he records the numbness, cramps and swelling of the legs together with headache, fever, palpitation, diarrhoea and terminal coma. Incessant pandemics of the disease clawed the country, and Tung Chi of the Sung dynasty (A.D. 960–1279) wrote a monograph on the subject which became the exemplar of many others.

In India it was scarcely less prevalent, and severe forms of it have been widespread in Africa for many centuries. It is not easy for anyone who lacks first-hand experience to appreciate how saturated with disease many primitive populations can be, especially in the tropics. Even today innumerable Africans are walking museums of pathology and it is common to find persons who, in addition to chronic dysenteric infections, have either malaria or yaws or both, whose eyes are diminished by trachoma and who harbour two or three distinct species of helminthic parasites yet whose most obtrusive symptoms may be due to a severe shortage of the vitamin B complex.

This multiple pathology is characteristic of the deficiency diseases. Several may coexist in one person and apart from the specific avitaminoses there is that general kind of deficiency or malnutrition due to individual or regional poverty. The burial grounds of antique populations yield unlimited evidence of intermittent or chronic starvation. It can be recognized in the structure of dental enamel, in radiographs of bones, and in the proportions of skeletal build. All early peoples died young and the rapid deterioration of health which was almost universal after the first two decades of life was largely the result of chronic malnutrition in childhood. From classical to medieval times many references to famine years are recorded. Sometimes it was

Plates 74, 75

Plates 78, 79

the harvest which failed through foul weather or because the ergot fungus (*Claviceps purpurea*) ruined the wheat or rye; sometimes an epizootic such as rinderpest or swine fever killed the herds and destroyed the only precious source of animal protein. A succession of these famines over a few generations or even a few years may so devitalize a population that they lose their initiative, decline into a submissive languor and fall easy victims to conquest by vigorous, well-fed enemies. There is skeletal as well as documentary evidence for thinking that the great conquests of Attila, Tamerlaine, the Iroquois League and Chaka's Zulu were achieved by groups who, at least temporarily, were experiencing fewer famine episodes than the nations they overpowered. This brings us close to the dictum of Johann Frank (1745–1821) that 'slave people are cachectic people'.

DENTAL DISEASE

For there was never yet philosopher
That could endure the toothache patiently
WILLIAM SHAKESPEARE

No structures of the human body are more likely to disintegrate during life than teeth, yet after death none have greater tenacity against decay. In consequence vast numbers survive from ancient burials to be the objects of envious study by elderly edentulous anthropologists. Contrary to popular belief, dental decay and loss are not exclusively the freight of civilized jaws; both are older than man himself, though few animals rival him in their liability to tooth disease. The pathology of these organs is similar to that of other tissues and they may be affected by congenital anomalies, injury, infections, new growths, degenerations or deficiency states. It is not surprising therefore that dentists and their work figure prominently in early medical literature as far back as the Ebers medical papyrus, since the long and painful history of toothache goes back to the Australopithecine ape men and beyond.

Oral disease is intimately related to habits of diet and the dentition of any person or group illumines much that might otherwise remain obscure about their way of life. The fact that the frequency of dental caries in the Swartkrans and Sterk fontein Australopithecines was more than one per cent and that the modern type of decay on the biting surface of the tooth was found amongst them probably means that more than a million years ago these hominids had already embraced an omnivorous diet. Java man, the Neandertals and the Aurig nacians in their turn all show carious lesions, albeit rarely. The stinking mouth rot of the Rhodesian Man has been mentioned in a previous section, but he was exceptional and it is only with the transition to a neolithic pattern of food production and its consequent revolution in eating habits that a marked increase in dental decay is found.

The reason for the relative immunity of early groups is not entirely clear because the teeth of these archaic individuals were almost universally faulty in their micro structure. This con trasts with the micro perfection found in wild rhesus monkeys and makes it likely that early man may in fact have been very *susceptible* of decay and would have developed much more of it had he been exposed to the oral environment of modern popula tions. The recent example of Tristan da Cunha leaves no doubt that freedom from caries need not imply an inherent resistance to it. Unlike the sectorial jaw of carnivores, in which the biting action is that of a shears, the human mandible acts as a suspended millstone where rotary grinding movements play a major part. It seems that, in general, Palaeolithic man exerted a greater chewing compression on his teeth than did the Neolithics or their successors and in doing so produced modifications of the occlusal surface that led to his low rate of caries.

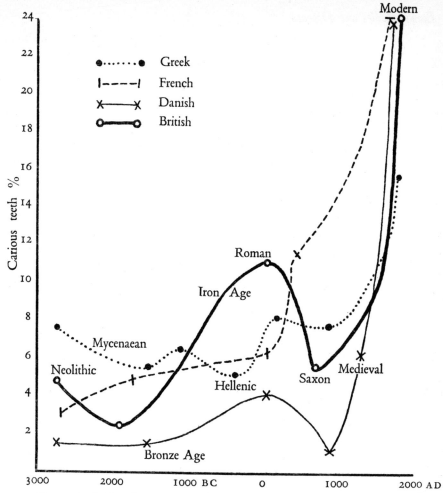

Fig. 19. Graph: Dental caries rates from Neolithic times to the present.

The incidence of tooth disease varies greatly at different European sites but it is less interesting to contrast unrelated enclaves than to trace the fluctuations that harrowed the inhabitants of large geographical areas. Figure 19 shows the frequency of carious teeth from the Neolithic Age to the present in Britain, Denmark, France and Greece.

Fig. 19

The over-all trends are not greatly dissimilar for the four countries, except that the range of variation for the Greeks is less than the others. Their low modern figure is especially interesting and is partly due to the inclusion of a large number of Athenians who still enjoy much of the immunity from dental infection that blest their Hellenic ancestors. Two factors contribute to this: a high fluoride content in the teeth and a low level of selenium. The first is well known as a protective agent and the fact that Athenian water is low in fluoride indicates that they derived it from other items of diet, perhaps fish. Recent work has shown that decay increases with heavy concentrations of selenium in the food. This may be why many of the millet-eating peoples have foully carious teeth because the grain sometimes contains the high level of four parts in ten million. The Athenians have a very low selenium intake both from their diet and the local water.

The influence of food on dental health can be illustrated by a brief survey of some American groups. The aboriginal Californians though exclusively food-gathering were the most omnivorous of American tribes. In addition to their staple diet of different kinds of acorn meal, together with fish and molluscs where available, they ate grasses, clover, berries, pine-nuts, prickly pear, sunflower, yucca, snakes, lizards, gophers, insects, larvae and much else. On this diet about a quarter of all skulls are found to harbour carious teeth, a sharp contrast with the extremely low incidence among Sioux buffalo-eaters or its seventy-five per cent in Zuni maize-growers. Agriculturists in eastern Texas had about double the amount of cavitation and tooth loss that affected the nomadic food-gatherers and hunters in the north and central parts of the state, whilst in the cave-dwellers to their west more than eighty per cent of skulls show ante-mortem loss of teeth, in addition to which these people had a high rate of alveolar abscesses as a result of severe dental attrition exposing the pulp cavity. These findings reveal the general tendency of flesh-eaters to have less caries than the growers of carbohydrate, whether corn, rice, manioc or yams. In the west Texan cave-dwellers scurvy was a prominent factor in their bad oral hygiene.

It is not only the content of food that influences decay; the method of its preparation and the total use to which teeth are put are also important. Many primitives regularly use their teeth as tools and much of their food is extremely coarse by our standards. In Europe from Roman to medieval times hand-querns of friable Niedermendig lava were in constant use; these shed scobs of grit into the flour which sometimes contained as much as three per cent of powdered stone. The feeding floors of pre-white Australians on the Murray River prove them to have been voracious cockle-eaters, as they still are. Their molar teeth wore down to the roots, which then turned over in the jaw but were still used as chewing surfaces until even the side of the roots became eroded. Trauma of this severity or even simple tooth fracture of the kind found in a Krapina Neandertal easily leads to infection of the tooth and, by extension, of its socket and surrounding bone.

Californian acorn-eaters pulverized their berries and leached out the astringent tannins with boiling water through a bed of sand, particles of which must have entered liberally into the flour. The Bodega midden showed contamination by coal grit. The Santa Barbara Amerindians using mortars of crumbly sandstone have more tooth damage than their neighbours whose querns were of tough fine-grained basalt. Grain-pounders of the type illustrated were also likely to shed abrasive *Plate 58* granules of quartz or felspar. The wear on the biting surface that is produced in this way is never uniform on all teeth; it is heaviest on the molar series, with a decreasing gradient of erosion from front to back. This attrition gradient is useful as an index for determining a person's age especially when the *Fig. 20* average pattern for his group is known.

Fig. 20. Gradient of dental attrition on a Medieval molar series.

Plate 78

Malnutrition in childhood leads to defects in the enamel of teeth—enamel hypoplasia. This takes many different forms but always constitutes a weakness and a potential focus of caries. The precolumbian Ketchipauan people often have multiple tiny cavities on the occlusal surface of their molars that are probably an expression of just such a fault in the enamel. Other agents of decay or tooth loss are also found. (The two conditions are partly, though not entirely, of independent origin.) In prehistoric skulls from Guam nearly all the women and two-thirds of the men had periodontal disease due to betel-chewing. This is a habit of addiction that produces permanent staining of the teeth ranging from orange to deep brown and is still valued by the women for the fine vermilion colour it imparts to the lips and tongue. Because the betel is mixed with lime, enormous accretions of tartar develop around the teeth and severe inflammation or ulceration of the gums ensues. In ancient Peruvians the caries rate is not exceptionally high but the loss of teeth from alveolar osteitis reaches an appalling level. Their diet included tomatoes, coca, maté, peanuts, potatoes, maize, dog and wild animals and would not be expected to produce a severely pathological mouth. Many of these pre-columbian mummies are found with little bags tied round their necks to contain coca leaves (*Erythroxylon coca*) which were chewed with a substance called *llute*, made of calcined shells, potato, and ashes of cacti or other plants rich in alkali. Thick green or brown accretions clustered on their teeth and gross damage to the alveolus occurred. In many cases fistular openings into the maxillary sinus show where abscesses have discharged their unctuous pus and this severity of infection appears to be due to a combination of causes. In the first place the cocaine alkaloid induces a necrosis of the periodontal tissues; secondly, it leads to a partial anaesthesia of the mouth so that sharp spicules of food or extraneous matter pass unnoticed when they wound the mucous membrane; and thirdly, an attitude of nonchalance and toleration towards these injuries results from the euphoric state of mind that was the divine gift of the cocaːchewer.

Plate 84

In some groups, such as the ancient Egyptians of Alexandria and the people of Merowe and Faras, there is evidence that toothpicks, brushes or other cleaning apparatus were used to promote oral hygiene. All too often this must have failed in its purpose and the dentist's help was sought. A IV Dynasty lower jaw survives from Giza in which an alveolar abscess may possibly have been drained by drilling two holes through the bone in precisely the way that is described in the Edwin Smith papyrus. But Egyptian dentistry never attained the high standard of Phoenician, Etruscan or even Roman work; amongst these peoples, especially the Etruscans, magnificent gold bridges were made to retain loose teeth in the jaw or to carry replacements for any that had been extracted. Numbers of these survive and we find early descriptions of them in the Hippocratic works, which also discuss alveolar abscess, necrosis of the gums, the difficult eruption of wisdoms and the teething ailments of babies. Aristotle speaks of extraction forceps and scalers as being instruments used by dentists; Celsus advises filling a large cavity in a tooth with lead before taking it out, so that the crown does not collapse in the grip of the forceps, and Archigenus (*c.* A.D. 100) records drilling the crown of a tooth in its most discoloured part to relieve pain. We can infer that gold crowning and bridgework were wellː established practices in ancient Rome because under 'The Laws of the Twelve Tables' (450 B.C.) it was forbidden to bury gold with a corpse except when it was in or around teeth.

The sum of all this evidence makes it plain that dental caries is immeasurably venerable amongst human diseases and that from Neolithic times countless jaws have been riddled with it.

MENTAL DISEASE

Who even dead, yet hath his mind entire.

EZRA POUND

To end this survey of the different types of disease we may glance at mental disorders. With the non-textual approach that is the main concern of this book it is not easy to find examples of psychopathology in the ancient world. If a man is mad we cannot know it from his bones, though the twenty-one freshly incised wounds in a skeleton at Aebelholt argue, from their position and the ferocity that flailed them on the victim, an acute maniacal fury in his assailant. Literary evidence abounds, for lunacy has always had a dreaded fascination for the sane, and many masterpieces from *Oedipus* to *Lear* and *Ghosts* have sought to probe the horror of a fugitive mind.

The therapy of these disordered psyches was prominent in ancient India and China under the solicitude of Buddhist medico-religious teaching, whilst in the West the early Greek philosopher-physicians veered more and more to the consideration of all aspects of psychological activity. Empedocles peered questingly into the sombre pavilions of a mind unloosed and is said to have cured a maniac with music. Whether Akhenaten was a mentally unbalanced mystic whose Aten-worship was a rhapsodic ecstasia is open to doubt but later classical writers give increasingly detailed case histories of famous patients. Soranus reports that the Abderites invited Hippocrates to their city in order to cure Democritus of his frenetic mania; Herodotus describes how the deluded and suicidal Cleomenes, whose raving may have been alcoholic dementia, had to be fettered by his relatives; the intractable sleeplessness, paranoid behaviour, hallucinations and self-deification of the emperor Caligula sprang from a mind shattered by an attack of ence-phalitis (sleepy sickness) at the age of twenty-five.

Discriminant subtlety in mental disease has been achieved only in recent decades and we cannot always sift the confusion of ancient accounts. Mania and melancholia were the symp-toms that most occupied the classical authors, who often treated these conditions with hellebore. Asclepiades of Bithynia (*fl.* 110 B.C.) rehashed earlier philosophical concepts to dis-tinguish between hallucinations and delusions. Hysteria was recognized and many symptoms that are obviously of hysterical or neurotic origin are recorded on tablets from the temple of healing at Epidaurus. The name *hysteria* comes from the Greek word for a uterus and at times the condition appears to have been viewed as the whimsy of an almost consciously capricious womb, but in general the attitude to insanity is vague probably because it was anciently felt to be possession by a god or spirit (awful though not necessarily evil) rather than a disease. From this it is a short step to those theories which see trepanation as a gesture to liberate an immanent cacodemon. But rational ideas gradually eroded the older mysticism. Celsus foreshadows the modern approach to lunacy when he urges that 'men who are bereft of their wits should be agreed with more often than thwarted', though in addition to narcosis with opium and hyoscyamus he also prescribed an apple of mandra-gora to be placed under the patient's pillow.

It is when we seek to augment the textual sources with other evidence and to recognize insanity in non-literate societies that our ingenuity is teased. Schizophrenia and obsessional states are not easily represented in any form of plastic art for the obvious reason that in everyday life they are manifest in beha-viour, not appearance. The frenzy of Dionysian and Cory-bantic rites is shown on Greek vases but these were fleeting episodes, self-induced, like the trance of the Pythian priestess when she inhaled the heady and heavy fumes that rose to enswathe her from the belching omphalos of the Delphic shrine. A fifth-century Byzantine mosaic at Ravenna which shows Christ casting out devils in the form of swine is a fore-runner of many portrayals of demoniacal possession, but these are comments by the artist on a supposed abnormality: the patient himself rarely looks in any way freakish. In another mosaic, however, the Daphni Pantokrator, it is tempting to think that the tense lips and jaw, the alert and apprehensive eyes reflect a chronic anxiety neurosis in the man who posed as model for the composition. Indeed, Byzantine mosaicists appear to have been often attracted to the delineation of this mental disorder.

Plate 85

Amongst the precolumbian ceramics of the Peruvian Mochica culture many erotica are found. They have been interpreted as the vented sewage of minds diseased and per-verted by the injury of artificially deforming the head. The same judgement has been passed on the little-known erotic wood-carvings of Salish, Nootka and other north-west coast tribes. But the majority of these pots show only variants of hetero-sexual behaviour and few modern psychologists would regard them as abnormal. A very small number display homosexual practices or bestiality; opinions will vary about these but at least they should be judged against the background and customs of the society that produced them and not in terms of the taste or ethos of any narrow religious or moral coterie of our own cultural heritage.

CHAPTER IV

Skeletal Adaptations

Partly adjust, amend and heal.

ALL DISEASES are adjustments made by the body to the environment—using that term in its widest sense to include internal as well as external influences. But not all adjustments are pathological, and without an obvious ha-ha to warn us where the bounds of normality will be over-stepped it is hard to determine the value of many deviations. The inflamed and thickened bone, covered with puffy, tender flesh that constitutes a bunion and which is due to ill-fitting shoes is, at least to the woman who hobbles around with it, grillingly abnormal. It is arguable, however, whether an exag-gerated curvature of the lateral metatarsal bone, resulting from a tight sandal thong, is a traumatic lesion or is only a graceful yielding, as it were, to mild external pressure. Skeletal adapta-tions of this sort often appear in early cemeteries and it is ap-propriate to glance at a few of them.

Fig. 21

The bowed metatarsal is a case of passive accommodation and in this it resembles the transverse groove on the skulls of Ainu which is supposedly due to carrying weighty objects in a head-sling. The bunion was an active response of the tissues and many similar reactions might be quoted. One of the most frequent is an anterior and upward extension of the ankle joint, the so-called 'squatting facet' that develops in persons who conduct many of their daily activities in a crouching posture. These facets are present in hundreds of native tribes today, as well as in ancient populations. Unusually deep ones are found in pre-white Hawaiians and we may infer that, when not walking or lying down, these people spent almost their whole

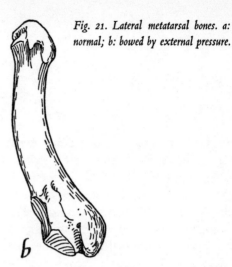

Fig. 21. Lateral metatarsal bones. a: normal; b: bowed by external pressure.

lives squatting or seated with their feet in a position of extreme dorsiflexion. In Britain they were common in the first Saxon invaders but much less so in late Saxons, a difference which reflects the more extensive use of chairs, benches and tables in the later period. When a squatting facet is present in a person of post-conquest date it probably indicates his low social or economic status. Two other conditions are sometimes associated with these facets: platymeria and platycnemia. The first is a fore-and-aft flattening in the upper third of the femoral shaft, the second is a side-to-side flattening of the tibia. Both conditions abound in early cemeteries but they do not necessarily appear together in a single individual, nor are they always present where squatting facets are found. They are rare in western Europe today but in the neolithic chambered tumulus burials of France and Britain both are obtrusive, especially platycnemia which amongst these peoples produces a cheese-cutting shin that is seldom exceeded in any other part of the world. The history of these traits is a long one. Platymeria is

Fig. 22

Fig. 23

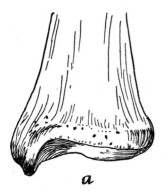
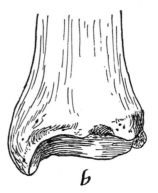

Fig. 22. Two tibiae. 'a' shows the modern European pattern; 'b' has a 'squatting facet' on the front of the ankle joint.

common in the Cro-Magnons; at the palaeolithic site of Pred-most in Moravia, where several dozen individuals have been discovered among the remains of more than a thousand mam-moths, extreme degrees of platycnemia occur. From their occa-sional association with squatting facets it has been thought that these conditions are due to habits of crouching. But powerful arguments can be advanced against this view and genetic or even pathological causes have been invoked as well as other postural or occupational influences. There is no uniformity of opinion but it is difficult to resist the conclusion that these skeletal features, like many others, are modified if not initiated by

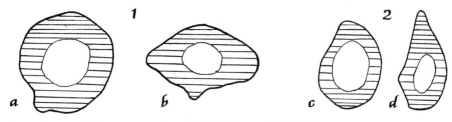

Fig. 23. Contrasts in the transverse sections of (1) thigh bones and (2) shin bones.

peculiarities of muscle action. The early Saxons of East Anglia often have marked flattening of their thigh bones but their faceted shins rarely show any extensive degree of lateral com/ pression, a circumstance that is not easily related to what is known of their daily occupations.

In some of these Anglo/Saxons the upper end of the femur carries a low bony ridge, like a lilliputian long barrow, on the front of the shaft. It is produced by a squeezing action of the muscles that hug the bone as the body swings to and fro in the heave and drag of hoeing and mattocking the clay/clodded seed/beds. This osseous hummock easily escapes notice but when found it gives the discerning archaeologist a more vivid realization of the arduous pangs of ancient farming than all the illuminations in the Luttrell psalter. To look at this moulded bone is to feel the ache and bite in one's own thigh.

An even more vigorous reaction is seen in the humerus of people who, from early childhood, use the sling as a weapon of war or the hunt. The most famous slingers of the classical world were the Balearic islanders whose prowess in Hannibal's army greatly impressed the Romans. Strabo (63 B.C.–A.D. 23) describes the different kinds of sling used by these peoples and their training in its use. He says: 'They would not even let their youngsters have any bread until they had first managed to swipe it with a sling/shot.' The weapon is depicted on Assyrian murals and an illustration of a naval battle during the reign of Rameses III (*c.* 1200 B.C.) shows its use by the Egyptian soldiers who man the fighting/tops of the ships. The powerful deltoid muscle that is developed by slinging produces

Fig. 24 a strong lateral curvature of the humerus and rough nodosities on its surface together with a splitting of the deltoid insertion eminence into two parts. This derives from the antagonized backward sweep and forward whirl which are the dual functions of the muscle when using this weapon, in contrast to the simpler stresses imposed on archers or spearmen.

Fig. 24. Humerus of a Balearic slinger showing lateral curvature. Normal bone for comparison.

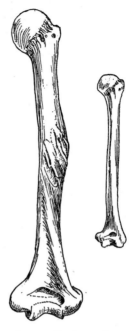

Peculiar modifications of the joints and muscle insertions are found in the legs of Ancient Greek mountaineers and a characteristic system of ridges on the rear of the skull has been described in dense forest dwellers who, with blowgun and arrow, scan the green mansions above them with their heads ever tilted back in search of arboreal game. An *ostracon* from Deir el Bahri, now in the Metropolitan Museum, New York, shows a very round-shouldered harper; a first impression of it suggests tuberculosis of the spine but it is more likely to be an occupational adaptation due to faulty posture while playing his instrument.

Many instances of this kind could be quoted. The distal end of the arm bone is sometimes perforated by a small hole, the epitrochlear foramen, a feature that is especially common in early Libyan and other African groups. It has been thought

Fig. 25

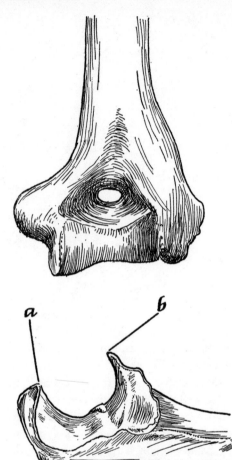

Fig. 25. Congenital perforation (epitrochlear foramen) in a humerus.

to result from grain-pounding, metal-working, bush-felling and similar occupations in which vigorous use of the elbow jars the olecranon and coronoid processes of the ulna with sharp impact against the humerus. In reality it is almost certain that this hole is partly congenital in origin although some jobs undoubtedly modify it when present. Among the Ashanti it is common to find that the mastoid region of the skull is heavier and more sturdy in females than in males, a reversal of the normal proportions. In these people it is the women who carry water-pots or other articles on their heads, and burdens of half a hundredweight or more are not unusual. Their thickened mastoids are a 'buttress' response to the down- thrust of the weights they support and the overdevelopment of the muscles attached to the mastoid processes.

Much caution is needed when diagnosing modifications of this kind. It has been thought that the thin legs and thick arms of Tucuna and other Amazonian Indians are the result of successive generations having passed most of their lives in canoes, paddling energetically with their arms whilst their legs atrophied from disuse. This not only presumes the inheritance of acquired characters, it violates the facts of ethnography. The example of a young pre-Ptolemaic Egyptian woman from Saqqara is instructive in a different way. Her spine was dis- tinguished by multiple abnormalities throughout its length, with fusion and flattening of vertebrae, wedge-shaped deformi- ties and accessory ribs. The excavator wrote an elaborate paper about this case stating that her abnormalities were due to severe and excessive use of the spine during childhood. He concluded that the girl had been trained as an acrobat from an early age, which accorded neatly with the evidence of dynastic murals where contortionists are sometimes shown. The truth is less florid. This woman's backbone is a perfect example of Klippel-Feil disease, a rare congenital condition which passed unrecognized here as it did again in the spine of the man with the trephination from Crichel Down and in a precolumbian from Paucarcancha, Peru. This, too, was diag- nosed as due to injury in early life.

CHAPTER V

Cannibalism

*To be knav'd out of our graves, to have our sculs made
drinking-bowls . . .*
THOMAS BROWNE

B Y NO STRAINING OF DEFINITIONS can cannibalism
be called a disease. It is an acquired taste just as respect-
able as, and far less surprising than, a penchant for Coca-Cola.
We are concerned with it here only because the burial grounds
sometimes yield skeletal evidence of the feast. But although
there is little doubt that cannibalism has a long history and has
been widely practised, its precise identification from surviving
bones is rarely accomplished. This is in sharp contrast to the
frequency with which some archaeologists claim to recognize
it. Indeed, a psychologist might pardonably wonder whether
their repeated identification of the custom is not the projection
of a subconscious wish to devour detested colleagues.

The Bible tells that when Benhadad, king of Syria, laid waste
the land of Samaria so that 'the fourth part of a cab of dove's
dung' sold for five pieces of silver, a woman in the pinch of
famine boiled her son and ate him. This may be nothing more
than the windy gossip of the chronicler, but Herodotus records
with convincing objectivity that the Scythian Massagetae
favoured their old and decrepit relatives with ritual death and
cooking. Strabo and other writers confirm the custom for the
ancient world, Marco Polo described it in China and Tibet
during the Middle Ages, whilst in recent times it has been
common in all continents except Europe. It was practised
almost universally by the Australian aborigines and widely
throughout Melanesia and Polynesia. The African distribution was irregular but still common. In the New World it

appears sporadically from north to south, including the area of the Caribbean which provided even the name of the custom.

It is not our purpose here to analyse the motives which foster anthropophagy. To realize that they are many we need only contrast a reluctant Kwakiutl ritualist who, at the end of the ceremony, vomits back the gobbets he has swallowed, with a cultured and fastidious gourmet of Vanua Levu or a protein-starved Niam-Niam of Central Africa. There are two charac-teristic pieces of evidence on which a diagnosis of cannibalism is commonly based: unnatural scattering of bones and the finding of them in a damaged condition, which usually means splintered long bones (allegedly to retrieve the marrow) or a defective skull base (on the supposition that the cannibal was a connoisseur of human brains). In most cases where the sug-gestion has been made there is little to support it. Bones may be broken or scattered from a variety of causes, and defective skull bases, far from being a reliable sign of cannibalism, are such a common result of inhumation decay that we are lucky if any long series of skulls is unaffected. There are, however, contexts where the evidence is strong. The earliest is among the Australopithecine hominids of South Africa, another is in the Chou Kou Tien Pithecanthropoids. Here the combination of heads severed from trunks and post-mortem as well as ante-mortem damage is conclusive for some form of head-hunting and at least suggestive of cannibalism. The evidence of forty-five bodies from Sha Kuo T'un is similar. But mutilation need not imply that the bodies were eaten. Undoubted examples of post-mortem dismemberment have been identified, one of the best known being the young man who was the primary neolithic burial at Maiden Castle, Dorset. After death his skull and most long bones had been crudely hacked with a sharp instrument but no snippet of evidence suggests that he was either cooked or eaten. Post-mortem dismemberment was typical of Huron burials and the Maiden Castle body need be no more than a ritual interment of this kind. In Denmark the idea of cannibalism was first proposed by King Frederick VII, an amateur archaeologist whose eminence conferred a cachet of respectability upon the diagnosis. Thereafter it became fashion- able throughout Scandinavia and Furst not only claimed several examples but also proposed scalping for a neolithic skull from Alvastra. More recently both practices have been accepted on exceedingly flimsy evidence for the Danish Ertebølle period.

Ranging more widely, we find the custom receives somewhat stronger support in the Pyrenean Upper Palaeolithic and in neolithic cave burials at Niah, Sarawak. Ehrhardt has made a restrained suggestion of it at Langhnaj, Gujarat, where a group of slaughtered mesolithic people comprising thirteen men, women and children has been found with bashed heads and cut limb bones, apparently buried under the floor of their living-huts or only just beyond the threshold. Despite the known frequency with which the Australian aborigines have practised it within recent decades no clear archaeological evidence of it from pre-white sites has been identified. Parenthetically we may note that in Australia and elsewhere human flesh was often consumed not fresh but as carrion in an advanced state of putrefaction. Eyewitnesses relate that no ill effects result and it is only our undue sensitivity that makes us suppose they should. Where the stench of the dead barely exceeds the odour of the living the imaginary disorders of a squeamish stomach are unlikely to occur. America offers what is perhaps the most convincing of all skeletal evidence of cannibalism and which corroborates the literary accounts of it among the Aztecs of Mexico. At Azcapotsalco a large red and yellow bowl has been found which contained human hambones and both there and at Teotihuacan shallow dishes made from skull tops augment the impression of probable blood-drinking and flesh- eating.

CHAPTER VI

Trephination

FEW SUBJECTS FASCINATE more strangely than pre-historic trephination or trepanning. Even today, with every help that science can offer, an operation to open the skull remains a pageant of drama and suspense and we are right to marvel at the neolithic patient who risked his life beneath the surgeon's flint. The splendour of endurance and boldness which are combined in that partnership commands our homage. But beyond the boldness of the deed there is an elusive quality about a trepanation which can only be appreciated by those who have seen it done.

In that ghastly moment when the Aztec priest ripped open his living victim on the stone of sacrifice he must often have felt the convulsive beats, made huge with panic, of the heart torn hot and steaming from its crypt. Did his fingers, even as the last shrieks fell to silence in the unfolding dawn around him, ever linger in awe and wonderment on that throbbing organ as he executed his horrible design? We cannot tell, but surmise would have it so. By contrast the scene at a trephination carried a lighter burden of terror, even for the patient. It is at least clear that not only was recovery the goal, it was also the rule. But here, too, the mystique of the unfamiliar must surely have spun its web across the onlooker. Less violent than a cardiac avulsion, a trephination may from its more tranquil nature have been more swathed in mystery. As the tables of the skull were slowly pared away to reveal an increasing expanse of the dura mater what strange compelling thoughts possessed the bystanders? There is an unexpected quality about that moist membrane, silvery grey and faintly striate. Here are no heaving paroxysms to rack and break a heart. Instead, the soft pulsations of the naked dura seem in their gentle surge to enfold a greater magnetism and to vamp with irresistible allure. No wonder that many writers believe that primitive man per-formed this operation with magic in his mind: a brief survey of the evidence counsels hesitation before succumbing too readily to this opinion.

The first prehistoric trephination to be discovered seems to have been found at Cocherel, France, in 1685 but it was not recognized as such for nearly two hundred years, and although the first early example was identified by the French surgeon and anthropologist Paul Broca in 1867 it was a Peruvian not a French skull on which he made the diagnosis. It was he, too, who advanced the doctrine that many cases were done with magical or ritualistic intent; a view which finds support in the fact that amulets made from discs of human skull and

Fig. 26 intended perhaps as charms or talismans have been found in large numbers in the same cultural context. Trephined crania appear in widely scattered places but by far the greatest numbers occur in two areas: neolithic western Europe, especially the Cevennes and Seine-Oise-Marne regions of France, and in precolumbian South America, in Peru and Bolivia. One of the earliest examples comes from an Early Danubian site (about 3000 B.C.) at Cannstadt, Stuttgart.

The operation has always been well known because the Hippocratic work *On injuries to the head* gives precise rules for how and when it should be done. Later writers such as Celsus (c. 42 B.C.–A.D. 37) add further details, whilst Paulus Aegineta quotes with approval Galen's nonchalant quip that trephinations can be done so safely with his special instrument that the meninges could not be damaged 'even if the surgeon is half asleep'. Arabic doctors preserved the ancient knowledge and handed it on to medieval surgeons in the West. Hippo-

Fig. 26. Rondelle of cranial bone excised by trephining. Neolithic.

crates does not suggest that the operation was done for ritual purposes or, as some writers have supposed, to release 'the demons of disease'. His aim was the practical one of treating wounds and there is evidence that the neolithics performed it for the same reason. Trepanned skulls showing injury and traumatic osteitis have been found at Rousson (Gard), Bray-sur-Seine (Marne) and Kellerød, Zealand, whilst many of the Peruvian examples were apparently done to treat depressed fractures caused by the sling shot and star-headed maces that were the characteristic weapons of that time and place. Indeed, several writers have pointed out the close geographical correlation between the practice of trepanning and the use of the sling as a weapon. It has also been asserted that prehistoric trephinations were designed to cure epilepsy ('the sacred disease'), convulsions and madness. If this were so, and it may well have been, palaeopathology can yield no vestige of proof apart from those cases where these conditions might themselves result from depressed fractures of the skull. It is likely, however, that the operation was used to treat intense headache due to various causes. The Tarkhan (Egypt) skull had mastoid disease in conjunction with its trephination and in one or two American cases the frontal sinus has been opened as if in an attempt to relieve the pain of chronic sinusitis. A skull of late Cortaillod date from Collombey-Muraz, Switzerland, shows an astonishing trephination through the right eye-socket. In this specimen the roof, medial wall and floor of the orbit have been incised and both the frontal and maxillary sinuses opened. To accomplish this the eye must have been removed and it is not surprising that no trace of healing is present.

This leads to the consideration of the frequency with which the operation was done, and the death rate from it. At the Neolithic site of Saint Martin-la-Rivière (Vienne) sixty skulls were found of which five (eight per cent) had been trephined. Prunières recovered a hundred and fifteen such crania from sites in Lozère, which must have been at least as high a percentage of his total. Comparable frequencies appear in Peru and it is clear that the operation was undertaken with an assurance bred of familiarity. Survival rates, which can be judged from the degree of healing round the margin of the hole, vary with the type of operation. It could be done by scraping, cutting or drilling and also by sawing. Many examples are combinations of different methods. When square or rectangular plaques of bone were removed by sawing the recovery rate tended to be low. It was a technique rarely practised outside Peru though sporadic examples, as at Lachish, Israel (600 B.C.), and a quite exceptional European specimen from Lisières (Deux-Sèvres), are occasionally found.

Fig. 27

The master trepanners were the Peruvians. Three-quarters or more of all their operations show that the patient survived his ordeal but the most convincing proof of the expertise of those ancient surgeons and of the trust they inspired in their clients is the occurrence of multiple trephination holes, done on different occasions. It is not unusual to find crania which have submitted to the procedure two or three times: the Pattalacta specimen has five such openings and one from Cuzco has seven, all well healed. The size of some of the openings is further proof of the operator's dexterity. In one from Saint Urnel (Finistère) the top of the skull had been removed in successive operations until the final opening was 160 mm. long in its sagittal arc and 125 mm. wide transversely ($6\frac{1}{4}$ in. × 5 in.);

Plate 80

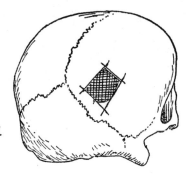

Fig. 27. Square trephination, unhealed.
Lachish, Iron Age.

about eighteen square inches of bone had been removed. Herniation of the brain through a large cranial aperture such as this is a well-recognized surgical calamity and it would be interesting to know what steps were taken to avoid this happening. Little information is available, but there are a few Peruvian examples where the hole in the skull has been covered by a plaque of shell or gold, and Moodie thought that a woman from Coyungo had even been the recipient of a successful bone graft. But the evidence here does not justify this dramatic conclusion. In some cases where the absence of healing shows that the patient died a few days after being trephined the death may have been due to wounds or injuries that have left no skeletal record and many unhealed examples can probably be explained as the post-mortem performance of the operation to procure amulet rondelles or as an exercise in which the student, then as now, could practise on the dead before being licensed to perform on the living.

Apart from the main French and Peruvian concentrations there is a thin but far-flung scatter of the custom with the specimens varying greatly in date. The earliest definite ones are the Danubian I group but two recently discovered skulls from Taforalt, Morocco, very strongly suggest that the operation was known there in Mesolithic times. In the British Isles about a dozen examples have been found, one of which, of the Beaker

Plate 81

period from Crichel, Dorset, is unusual in that the rondelle was scrupulously replaced over the hole from which it had been excised. In Eire the monastery of Nendrum (*fl.* 450–974) has yielded one, and another comes from the medieval cemetery of Collierstown, Meath. Frankish and Merovingian examples are found and a Scandinavian group includes specimens from Lundtofte, Denmark (Bronze Age), Västeras, Sweden (Iron Age), and Gotland (Viking Age). In a passage grave context at Sjolmen, Scania, trephinations have been described that were apparently done after death to convert the skull into drinking-cups. Outliers are recorded from Furninha, Portugal, the Canary Isles, the Caucasus and Kiev; and a mummified head with a large occipital trephination was found at the south Siberian Han period cemetery of Oglakty. Another, of uncertain provenance, is in Vladivostok museum.

Many of the Peruvian trepanations have a geometrically regular area of osteitis, angular in shape, around the hole. There is some reason to believe that this is due to the total excision of a large piece of the scalp before starting to remove the bone. The fact that the osteitic area is abruptly limited in this unnaturally angular way indicates that the wound was dressed with some chemical valued for its antiseptic properties and this may partly account for the high recovery rate. Although most Peruvian mummies were simply dried, a few were preserved by balsams, resins, tannins and other substances which the surgeons may also have used as wound dressings. At Chan Chan and Recuay precolumbian pottery vessels showing trephination have been found but they add nothing to our knowledge of the subject. Great caution is needed in diagnosing this operation: holes in the skull can be due to many different conditions and to decide between them is often difficult. Confusion may arise from congenital lacunae, accidental or deliberate injury, tuberculous and syphilitic necrosis, some dozens of different tumours and a variety of other lesions.

Holes nibbled by small rodents often look like a trephination
when the tiny tooth marks are later smoothed by soil action,
and many Greenland Eskimo crania mimic the operation
when humidity, high winds and the weight of the skull com-
bine to erode post-mortem apertures through the vault. Each
example should be studied with care and none accepted as
surgically induced unless there is positive evidence for doing so.

Plate 82

A trephined skull from Strupcice, Czechoslovakia, also
displays another type of injury—sincipital-T. This condition,
which was first recognized in a skull from the Dolmen de la
Justice, Epône (Seine-et-Oise), commonly takes the form of
a broad line of inflammatory reaction starting on the frontal
bone and extending to the back of the parietals where it splits
into two transverse branches. The long arm of the T is usually
broken into shorter lengths. The curious appearance of the
bone is not produced by sawing, scraping, cutting or drilling
but by cauterization, apparently by incising the scalp in dis-
continuous segments and pouring boiling oil or resins through
the openings on to the bone. The pattern of the scar varies
slightly over the wide geographical range in which the custom
occurs. Most examples of the typical T-shaped lesion come
from neolithic burials in north-west France but it has been
identified in Central Asia, in Africa and in Guanche skulls
from the Canary Isles where it inclines to an oval outline. An
example from Amazonas, Peru, was cruciate rather than T-
shaped. Almost all recorded specimens are in females. We can
only guess at its purpose in neolithic and precolumbian usage,
and whether it was primarily ritualistic or therapeutic cannot
now be known but knowledge of the procedure did not die
out. It survived into medieval times as a surgical operation
under the name of *purgatio capitis* and as such is described by
Avicenna, 'De cura melancholiae et quandoque opportet ut
caput ejus secundum crucem cauterizetur si nihil aliud confert'
(Canon I, III, tr. 4, cap. X).

Fig. 28

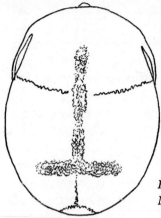

Fig. 28. Cauterization of the skull (Sincipital-T). Neolithic.

The extent to which trephination and sincipital-T burning were numbed by anaesthetics cannot be estimated. The facility with which skulls have been opened in recent years by primi- tive peoples such as Tibesti, Tahitians and Aymara proves that the operation can easily be done on fully conscious patients but the Stone Age inhabitants of France almost certainly culled plants from the juice of which they squeezed their drowsy anodynes and the Peruvians could always com- mand a divine euphoria by chewing a quid of coca. For the biggest trephinations these passports to ecstasia may have been needed.

CHAPTER VII

Radiographic Evidence

Every death is a new approach.
The image increasingly shifts,
Less to be touched, more translucent.

C. A. TRYPANIS

LOOKING AT THE DUST-DRY OBJECT which is the typical excavated bone, feeling its light brittleness of texture or its heavy mineralized compaction, it needs a leap of the imagination to see it again as it was in life. Used as we are to the vagaries of soil action and the metamorphoses of time which may whittle a bone to a wafer of egg-shell fragility or harden it to a stony baton, the image of what it once was eludes recall. Yet within the rippling muscles of a lithe Minoan bull-leaper, under the moon-glow skin of a Scythian princess, or supporting the black and sweating bodies of the men who wrought Zimbabwe were living bones, at once pliant and tenacious. And when a surgeon, with clean strokes of gouge and chisel, cuts into one the gush of blood from innumerable channels leaves no doubt that this is a tissue which is quick and spawning, drenched with the very sap of life. Within these same structures the essence of the blood is made—ten million red cells fresh born every second, a miracle of inexor-able vitality. It is not surprising therefore that disease may smutch the interior as well as the surface of bones. When this happens the simplest way to investigate it is by radiography and, in palaeopathology no less than in disease of the living, many abnormalities must be diagnosed in this way.

Although most fractures are obvious as soon as a bone is handled, there are exceptions to this. Many are masked by callus, a proliferation of new bone which is thrown around the break when healing takes place. This callus cannot always be distinguished at a glance from sarcomatous tumours or calcification of a blood clot: radiography will resolve the doubt by disclosing the fracture inside the mass of new bone. Foreign bodies such as arrowheads are as a rule easily visible if they are embedded in any part of the skeleton. On rare occasions they may become obscured by a bony reaction which engulfs them and X-rays are needed to reveal what has happened. Non-specific infections such as periostitis and osteo-myelitis may be distinguishable only by examining the marrow cavity radiologically and the infections of some small and relatively inaccessible regions often escape recognition unless the part is radiographed. An example of this is the mastoid process. Normally a group of large air cells should be found in the bone. When this pneumatization is much reduced it is likely to be the result of previous infection in the middle ear and antrum. It is not every acute mastoid infection that produces destruction of the bone and a discharging sinus of the type

Plate I found in the Rhodesian man, but careful radiography of a series of Merovingians has enabled Morel and Demetz to identify mastoid infections in the absence of any striking ex-ternal change. It has been recognized in the same way in the Ozark Bluff people of Arkansas, a precolumbian Amerindian group living close to the bread line on sumach, ground acorns, ragwort, sunflower seeds, insects and small animals. Perhaps their precarious level of subsistence and a habit of crouching over charcoal fires (charcoal has been found in their dried faecal masses) combined to produce the high frequency of nasal sinusitis and mastoid infection which occurrred amongst them. Occasionally, resort to X-rays will confirm a doubtful case of tuberculosis in a vertebra or help the diagnosis of syphilis or leprosy.

Malignant growths are difficult to classify because of their variety and uncertain origin. Sarcomata often begin in bone, whereas tumours of the carcinoma type invade it by secondary extension from soft tissues. Radiography can distinguish between different types of growth. In multiple myeloma, a somewhat uncommon malignant process, visible areas of destruction penetrating the outer surface of the bones are usually far outnumbered by foci of the disease which can only be detected radiographically. Cancer deposits that invade bone often start from primary growths in the breast, prostate or thyroid and if, as frequently happens, the soft-tissue lesions kill the patient before the metastatic secondaries have broken through the surface of the bone these may remain unsuspected. Routine X-raying of skeletal remains might reveal that cancer was more common in early populations than is usually believed. There is also a form of cystic disease which can only be diagnosed with certainty in a radiograph.

When a limb is not used owing to paralysis, fracture, painful arthritis or some other cause, the bones undergo a process of rarefaction or partial decalcification analogous to a disuse atrophy. This rarefaction can be seen in an X-ray film and gives a clue to what has happened. It occurs even while abundant callus is being formed at the site of a fracture but with restored function consolidation returns to normal. In a Merovingian from Les Mémoires, Isère, who apparently died from a fall on his skull, it was possible to estimate an ante-mortem fibular fracture as having occurred about six months before death. The osteoporotic bone had disintegrated completely in the soil except for the dense area of callus in the region of the well-healed break. The opposite fibula of apparently normal density had survived undamaged, as the fractured one presumably would have done if it had had time to harden again under the stress of normal function. In a Late Saxon burial from Thorpe St Catherine, Norfolk, a radiograph of a pair of tibiae showed a rarefaction in one of them that was almost certainly due to poliomyelitis which left only a slight weakness in the muscles.

The affected bone was hardly distinguishable from its fellow on visual inspection but the radiological difference was immediately apparent. A special cause of osteoporosis is the diminishing use of limbs with advancing age. Conversely, vigorous muscular activity leads to thickening of the bone, not only in its external areas of muscle attachment but internally also to withstand stress. The difference can be shown radiologically in the relative proportions of the medullary cavity and its surrounding cortex. In an Anatolian Bronze Age pastoralist accustomed to herd his goats over rough mountain terrain the femoral medulla may be less than a quarter of the external thickness of the bone; in an old woman from the twelfth-century Gilbertine priory at Shouldham, Norfolk, the medulla occupies 88 per cent of the thickness, senile or pathological disuse having reduced the bone to a thin husk around the marrow cavity. When much variation in osteoporosis is found in a single community this may indicate segregation into different class, occupational or nutritional moieties. A medieval Japanese group near Yokohama seems to be separable into two social grades on this basis.

Fig. 29

The study of dental anomalies and disease is greatly dependent on radiographic investigation. In jaws and teeth which are intact conditions such as pulp-stones or periapical abscesses cannot be seen on simple inspection yet are important on account of their varying incidence in different populations. In a group of East Greenland Eskimo skulls Pedersen found that enormous pulp-stones were commonly present; in other groups, Patagonians, Ancient Egyptians and Avars for example, they seem hardly to occur. Fusion of tooth roots, usually of the second and third molars, is another character that is especially common in the Eskimo dentition. It has been suggested that this is due to severe lateral strains which are thrown on the teeth in mastication; a more likely explanation is that it is genetic in origin. It is a feature characteristic of the Neandertals

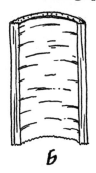

Fig. 29. Sections of thigh bones
a: of a mountain pastoralist;
b: of an elderly Medieval
religious.

a   **b**

—for example the St Brelade and Naulette specimens—and it is common in Lapps, Australians, Bushmen, Japanese and others. If it is genetic in origin the same can also be said of three-rooted lower molars which are yet another feature with high incidence in Eskimo skulls and one that shows their affinity with the Mongol race. Because dental pathology is intimately related to habits of diet and general nutritional levels a full radiographic examination of the jaws should always be made of any group that is being studied.

One of the most rewarding uses of radiography is in the examination of mummies. If these are intact in elaborate cartonnage packs or wrapped in friable bandages it may be the only possible access to them. Interpretation of the films, above all of Egyptian mummies, is bedevilled by intrusive sand, silt, resins, pieces of wood and other bric-à-brac which are mostly absent in natural sun-dried specimens and the simpler Peruvian packs. Even so, it is possible to obtain much information, though in order to do so exposure from several different angles may have to be made. Fractures can usually be seen without much difficulty and osteoarthritic lipping at the joints is also obvious. So, too, are dental abnormalities. Soft-tissue lesions present a much more complicated problem. The ideal way of investigating them is by dissection but often the archaeological value of the material forbids a destructive autopsy.

Pathological enlargement of organs can sometimes be seen, for example a malarial spleen, hydatid disease of the liver or the *cor bovinum* of heart failure. Displacements of the heart or kidneys are less easily detected but abnormal calcification of ligaments, muscles and especially the tortuous blood-vessels of arteriosclerosis is recognizable. With few exceptions any other soft-tissue diseases are revealed only in a most ill-defined and ambiguous way on radiographs.

It has already been stressed that we examine bones for precisely the same reason which prompts the study of any other aspect of archaeology: to reconstruct as far as possible the pattern of life led by ancient peoples. But there is a great difference between the information given by artifacts and that to be deduced from skeletons. A sequence of buildings on a site or a neat stratification of pottery types gives a continuing or perspective view of the men whose relics they are. Even a single object found in a grave can suggest something of the *habitual* behaviour of its owner. A rhyton or kylix implies convivial drinking parties; an aulos, musical soirées in Attic elegance; ushabtis whisper of reverence for the gods, whilst scramasaxes howl the blood-red eclipse of Apollo and his oracles at the close of the pagan world. A skeleton by contrast yields for the most part a briefer glimpse. It shows a man as he was at a single moment in time—the moment of death—and it gives a snapshot, not a moving picture. It reveals, more or less, the age at which he died, his dental condition at that instant, perhaps a fatal blow which struck him down or a tumour that brought about his end. All too often the bones appear to be normal and no hint of past illnesses or the cause of death can be found. In an attempt to penetrate this barrier and to obtain a more dynamic view of an individual's history a new technique has recently been devised.

During childhood and adolescence a typical long bone such as a radius or a tibia grows in a way which, stripped to its essentials, is as follows. At each end of the shaft or diaphysis is a distinct cap, the epiphysis, separated from it by a narrow zone of proliferating tissue called the growth cartilage. As this cartilage proliferates the older cells calcify and are replaced by newly formed bone. The continuation of this process leads to the elongation of the diaphysis by deposition at the two ends. Eventually a time comes when the growth cartilage ceases its activity and is replaced by bone. The epiphyses fuse with the shaft in a firm osseous union and no more linear growth is possible. If, during development, the bone is subjected to any adverse influence this process of active proliferation is disturbed and the growth cartilage remains dormant for an indefinite time depending on the kind of injury. This may be a short acute illness such as pneumonia or enteritis, or a more protracted episode such as a period of famine—especially, perhaps, protein starvation. With recovery, growth starts anew but it is found that a transverse line of dense calcification is left in the shaft to mark the plane of arrested activity of the cartilage. The simplest way to detect these 'bone scars' is by radiography. They are usually referred to as Harris's lines of arrested growth. At least two of them can be seen in the tibia of the blindfolded girl from the Windeby bog and four or five in that of the first mummy X-ray plate ever to be published in 1898, within three years of Roentgen's discovery. What is especially important about them is the fact that, except in certain relatively rare circumstances, they are permanent. In the event of repeated episodes of infection or starvation a series of Harris's lines may be formed and their total number and spacing give an approximate indication of the age at which these checks to growth occurred. It is essential to realize that the presence of these lines cannot ever be recognized by simple inspection and that in the vast majority of cases they are caused by diseases that leave no other detectable mark on the bones which appear therefore to be normal until they are X-rayed.

Plate 79

Here, then, is a method not only of estimating the incidence of disease in different individuals but also of comparing morbidity rates between populations. This can be done quite simply by calculating the average number of lines occurring in a selected bone from a sample of each. Striking and unexpected differences may be found. A series of several hundred tibiae of Early and Middle Saxon date from two sites in East Anglia was examined. At Burgh Castle an average of 2·6 lines per bone was found, at Caister-on-Sea 5·1. The places are only about five miles apart, so it is of great interest to speculate on why the total morbidity of the children at Caister was double that of their contemporaries on the other side of the Yare estuary. The Caister people lived in a squalid congested village at the water's edge; the Burgh Castle site is on higher ground and its cemetery probably served the surrounding farmsteads as well as the local community. It seems likely that greater dispersal of the inhabitants and perhaps a diet richer in milk and meat may explain the lower morbidity in this group. Let us stress once again that Harris's lines can be produced only during the growing period; they give no information about illness in adult life. It is also important to realize that although one of these bone scars shows that some morbid process has occurred it gives no clue to the nature of the illness. In the present state of our knowledge it does not even seem possible to distinguish between a line caused by a short acute illness such as measles and one which is the result of a three-month famine. Lines produced by scurvy may possibly be an exception to this statement.

So far this technique has been applied to only a few early populations. A group of Bronze Age pastoralists from Dorset had the low average of only 0·8 lines per bone. Again it is tempting to see this as an expression of the healthy conditions that result from people living in small, dispersed family groups with a good standard of diet and at a period when the climate was better than it is today. A dense urban population mostly of sixteenth, to mid nineteenth-century date from St Bride's, Fleet Street, London, had four times as many lines per bone as the Bronze Age community. It is axiomatic in studies of disease that climatic conditions will always be related to the type and amount of sickness that occurs in any population, so it is interesting to see what effect an extreme type of environ, ment might have on this index of morbidity. A group of skeletons of Kalahari Bushmen was examined, not only on account of the rigorous climate in that region but also because it appeared likely that periodic shortage of food might leave an especially clear record of Harris's lines. Surprisingly, very few were found: the average was only 0·3 for each individual. This must undoubtedly mean that infections were uncommon amongst them and here, too, the sparseness of the population was probably the reason for this. But if recurrent food shortages really did affect these people it is difficult to explain the low incidence of bone scars. One possible reason suggests itself. The condition of steatopygia has already been mentioned as occurring in Bushmen and Hottentots. Is it too fanciful to suggest that in times of famine their great rumps act as a sub, stantial reserve of calories which can be drawn upon to tide them over the critical period in much the same way as a camel has a storehouse in its hump?

Fig. 8

The estimation of relative morbidity rates of departed popu, lations does not exhaust the information obtainable from Harris's lines. The distance of any one of these scars from the end of the bone indicates the length of the shaft when it was produced, and from this the age of the child at that time can be inferred. Thus there is registered in the bone a record of the major illnesses that attacked the person during the first fifteen or sixteen years of life, together with the age at which they occurred. This gives a diachronic or perspective view of an individual's health that cannot be obtained in any other way.

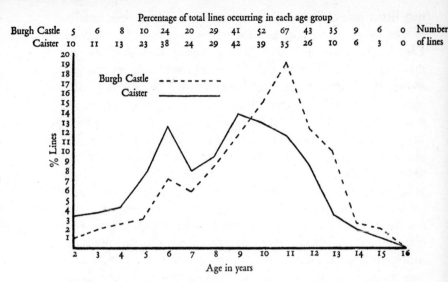

Percentage of total lines occurring in each age group

| Burgh Castle | 5 | 6 | 8 | 10 | 24 | 20 | 29 | 41 | 52 | 67 | 43 | 35 | 9 | 6 | 0 | Number |
| Caister | 10 | 11 | 13 | 23 | 38 | 24 | 29 | 42 | 39 | 35 | 26 | 10 | 6 | 3 | 0 | of lines |

Fig. 30. Graph: Frequency of Harris's lines of arrested growth in two Anglo-Saxon communities.

Having determined the age at which each line was laid down in every member of a sample it is easy to plot the percentage of all lines which falls in each year of age. When this is done it may be found that, as well as having different total morbidity rates, two populations have distinctive distribution patterns for these episodes. It has already been noted that the Caister Saxons had twice as much childhood illness as their neighbours at *Fig. 30* Burgh Castle. Figure 30 reveals the pattern of disease in terms of age incidence.

It shows that for each year of life until the age of nine the Caister people consistently get a higher percentage of their total morbidity than the Burgh Castle folk. For the rest of the growing period the waterside children have relatively less of their total illness affecting them than the dwellers on the high ground have. This means that the young people at Burgh Castle had a healthier start in life regardless of any illness that may have affected them later. If we separate the two sexes instead of grouping them together as was done in Figure 30 a new feature emerges. With the reduction in sample numbers which follows this splitting of the sexes it is safer to express the result in tabular form by lustra rather than by an annual graph.

Fig. 31

Sex	Percentage of lines occurring at age			Numbers of inhumations
	2 – 6+	7 – 11+	12 – 16	
Male	25·6	58·9	15·5	39
Female	41·7	50·0	8·3	36

Fig. 31. Harris's line incidence and age (Caister)

The total morbidity of the males and the females is almost identical at Caister, but Figure 31 shows that in the two- to six-year period the boys get only a quarter of all their illnesses, whilst the girls get two-fifths; in middle childhood there is no significant difference; in the final third of the growing phase only a tenth of their total morbidity affects the girls, whereas a sixth still remains to fall on the boys. No hint of this could be obtained by merely inspecting the bones and its revelation radiographically is a social document of great interest. At present the reason for this difference can only be a matter for speculation. Perhaps the most likely solution is that in a society devoted to an ethos of male dominance girls were less valued than boys and had, from an early age, to accept a lower status, to content themselves with the left-overs of the repast and accustom themselves to being the undernourished drudges of their menfolk. Some such structure within the family group may explain the apparent fact that the girls start getting their illnesses at an earlier age than the boys, despite the inherent advantage of their X—X chromosome pattern. Many more ancient peoples need to be examined in this way before a general picture of disease patterns can be obtained but a few further problems of the Caister group may be unravelled by the Harris's line method. The incidence of adult dental caries in the females is more than double what it is in the males. This probably means that it is not so much the total amount of illness which affects dental decay but the time of life at which it occurs. Tooth formation is especially active before the age of seven years; in this period the developing teeth are most vulnerable to systemic disturbance and the fact that so much more ill-ness affects the girls than the boys during these early years probably leads to the higher caries rate in later life. It may also produce a general constitutional weakness which would ex-plain why women eventually die younger than men. This suggestion has several advantages over the traditional explana-tion of obstetric hazards though the two are not, of course, mutually exclusive.

In spite of its present uncertainties it seems clear that the Harris's line technique will open up hitherto unsuspected vistas in the comparative epidemiology of prehistoric popula-tions.

CHAPTER VIII

Artificial Interference

Euclid alone has looked on Beauty bare.
Let all who prate of Beauty hold their peace.

EDNA ST VINCENT MILLAY

IN ALL AGES man seems to have been discontented with his body. Graced neither with the iridescent splendour of the lepidoptera nor the flamboyant plumage of the Paradiseidae, he has sought instead to enhance nature by art and in the pursuit of a kaleidoscopic ideal has flirted with the limits of ingenuity and the bizarre. Artificial interference with the body embraces an astonishing range of procedures from the titivation of an eyelash to the monstrous deformation of a whole skull, from nail painting with delicate crimson or silver lacquers to gross mutilations of hands and feet, from hair tinting to tooth ablation. Few places and fewer peoples can be found where the unadorned body either of man or woman has been viewed with satisfaction.

It may seem that these meddlings with nature are too marginal to the subject of disease to come within the compass of our study. This is not so. Many devices are so extreme that they can only be described as pathological from their inception, others tend ultimately to produce some abnormal condition and even the least of them may by chance go wrong: a plucked eyebrow can lead to an infected follicle, dyed hair evoke an allergic rash. Most of these procedures involve only soft tissues and so elude the palaeopathologist but some do affect the skeleton and are often encountered.

A normal adult skull has about it an aspect of such uncompromising rigidity that any attempt to alter its shape seems an act of extravagance and daring. Yet in infancy and childhood the cranium, like any other bone, is meekly plastic and can be coaxed and moulded like a swelling gourd. Indeed, a baby's skull is so malleable that many lop-sided occipital bones are produced quite unintentionally as a result of cradling habits. Where it is the custom to place a child lying on its back in a cradle, perhaps strapped in that position, it will usually try to turn its head slightly to one or other preferred side. Eventually flattening and asymmetry of the back of the skull result and remain through life. This seems to have happened among a group of Late Saxon people, perhaps of Friesian origin, at Red Castle, Thetford, Norfolk. Their heads are so flattened posteriorly that most of them can be laid resting on the occiput and remain perfectly steady. Almost all have a slight tilt to one side. Similarly unintentional deformations may result from the custom of dressing infants in bands and caps of various kinds, although it is not always possible to distinguish with certainty between accident and design. The classic country of the deforming head-dress is France. An early example, undoubtedly produced by tight bandaging, comes from a fourth-century A.D. site at Voiteur, Jura, and two others, both Early Iron Age, have been found at Corveis-siat. In each of these skulls the vault is drawn up into a conical shape and the distortion leaves no doubt that it was deliberately produced. The custom survived and as late as the end of the nineteenth century Delisle was able to examine over twenty-five thousand examples. Barbichets, serres-têtes and béguins were among local names for the different kinds of caps and bandages used to mould the children's heads. The principal regions where this custom prevailed were around Toulouse and in the departements of Seine-Maritime (where Delisle estimated that over ten per cent of the women and fifteen per cent of the men were deformed), and Deux-Sèvres. At Rouen he found deformation in nearly a third of his sample. The pattern of distortion varied in the different regions according to the kind of head-dress used. The toulousaine type was elongated in a backwards direction, with a sloping forehead. In Seine-Maritime a depression was produced in the frontal bone and this continued in a groove over the ears and down under the nape; the *cagnottes* of Albi drew the occiput into a point resembling the Voiteur type. In general, French head moulding reflects some degree of class distinction; it was chiefly practised and continued longest among the lower orders. Another European focus of this custom is Marken, Holland, where the use of a complicated child's cap continued well into the present century. It was worn by boys until the age of about six years and by girls for ten years longer. These examples are on the very doorstep of the present. The antiquity of the custom as far as Europe is concerned is less easy to decide. More than a century ago Robert Knox, perplexed by the strange appearance of the newly found Neandertal skull, suggested that it had been artificially deformed. Fifty years later Baudouin diagnosed a case from the French Neolithic at Belleville (S.-et-M.), but it was a doubtful example and even today with several candidates for inclusion no really un-equivocal specimen of that period can be found here.

Outside the area of western Europe the trait is distributed unevenly. It seems hardly to have been practised north of the Baltic but scattered cases are known from Poland and southern Europe. In *Airs, Waters, Places,* which is the first systematic treatise to deal with the effect of environment on health, Hippo-crates described a race of people called Macrocephali. He says that among these 'Longheads' as soon as a baby is born its head is moulded by hand and later by the use of bandages and appliances until it becomes drawn out in a unique fashion. He recorded too that the persons with the most extreme deformity were considered the noblest. In the Balkans and the Caucasus skulls have been found which closely resemble those described by Hippocrates. One of these dates from about 450 B.C. and although the likelihood is whimsically slender it is at least physically possible that its owner and the much-travelled author of *Airs, Waters, Places* could have stood face to face in mutual contemplation.

Further east the concentration again becomes heavy. Large numbers of crania, deformed far more severely than the western examples, have been recovered from the great plains area of south Russia stretching from the lower Dniester to the Volga and beyond, with excavations round Rostov, Kertch and Tiflis yielding many of the most extreme specimens. Few of these can be dated with any confidence to before the Christian era, most are some centuries later; but, leaving the mainland, two much older examples have been found in Crete in a definite neolithic context.

To bridge the gap into Asia, the occurrence of cranial deformation may be noted in Asia Minor and through Kurdistan to India where it was exceedingly common and, in contrast to France, consistently linked with high social status. It is found in Celebes and also Borneo where it is still practised. Here the deformation is produced by strapping the child into a cradle which has a special attachment designed to apply front-to-back pressure on the head. (A similar cradle apparatus was used by the Iroquois.) The result is a fronto-occipital shortening of the cranium which may eventually be no more long than wide, as in a skull found in the Philippines. A few cases have also been recovered from China, but the practice was uncommon there.

In Africa cranial deformation occurs widely but irregularly and nowhere are we teased by a more beguiling puzzle than in Egypt. From the long, waiting centuries of predynastic times no case is found; the glories of the Old Kingdom blossom and fade but they offer no example of the elliptic, mathematical beauty of a drawn-out skull. Then, quite suddenly, in that best-known yet most enigmatic of all Egyptian periods, in the

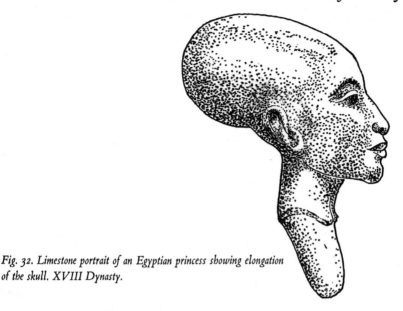

Fig. 32. Limestone portrait of an Egyptian princess showing elongation of the skull. XVIII Dynasty.

reign of Akhenaten the Heretic King, whose passionate worship of the Sun-disc still reaches out to us across the millennia with undimmed incandescence, the first hints are found. They do not come from bones or mummies but from the statues and bas-reliefs which abound from this el-Amarna period of the XVIII Dynasty. Looking at the portrait head of Akhenaten's daughter with its compelling resemblance to a vegetable marrow, we can scarcely doubt that it has been conjured into that shape by artifice. A difficulty arises, how-ever, when the mummies of the period are examined. None of them shows any evidence of such distortion. That of the presumed body of Akhenaten himself survives in a severely damaged state and his skull is indeed an unusual shape. It has some pathological condition which seems to be a mild and rather unusual form of acromegaly and this would prob-ably be enough to explain the curious shape in which it is

Fig. 32

shown upon his statues. The portrayal of the same shape in his daughters could be ascribed to heredity but this cannot explain why his wife and various court officials are also some, times shown with the same pattern of head. Another possibility is that these carvings are merely an artistic convention inspired, we may suppose, by the natural melon shape of the head of the king himself. This may be the first but it is certainly not the last occasion in history when subjects have aped the oddities or glossed over the imperfections of their sovereign. A further point which may have significance here is that some scholars have detected a suggestion of cranial deformation in a representation of Sety I at Abydos. His mummy survives, however, and shows that he had a perfectly normal skull. On balance it seems best to reject head-moulding as a native institution in dynastic Egypt until firm skeletal evidence is available. Some later examples have been found in Alexandria but they are of foreign type and may have originated in Syria; it is not until the sixth century A.D. that a definite Egyptian specimen occurs.

Among the principal head-moulding peoples of Africa are the Mangbetu of the Congo. Their form of distortion closely resembles that of the portraits from el-Amarna but here there is no doubt about its artificial nature. It is produced by coiling bandages and string around the child's head, and in later life the style of hair-dressing and head-gear skilfully accentuate the deformity. Here again, as among the BuShongo and the Ashanti, head-moulding was the prerogative of the nobility. Off the mainland, the Vazimba of Madagascar practised a fronto-occipital flattening. In Melanesia deformed skulls have been found in New Caledonia, the Loyalty Islands and Fiji. Great variations in form and frequency are found there. In the New Hebrides both Virchow and Hamy observed the resemblance of the type to some of the Peruvian forms. The custom is widely spread throughout Polynesia and in all these places still tends to go with high rank as it did in Old Hawaiians before the European discovery. The Samoans used pressure from three stones to produce a well-defined shape of head.

The most extravagant of all cranial deformations come from America. In general three methods were used: bandaging, which produced an annular shape; 'free-boards' strapped to the infant's head and resulting in an oblique fronto-occipital flattening; and binding the child on to a cradle board to produce a vertical flattening. Variations occur due to the use of accessory pads and other slight differences of technique. The custom had an extremely wide scatter in the New World. From the north-east we have already noted the Iroquois; the Adena people of Ohio and Kentucky also practised it. It is found among the Natchez of the lower Mississippi, the Nootka and Kwakiutl of the north-west Pacific coast, the Klamath of Oregon and throughout Mayan territory in southern Mexico and Central America. In South America three main regions predominate: the Caribbean coast of Colombia and Venezuela; the Pacific coast of Ecuador, Peru and northern Chile with the mountain hinterland; and the Patagonian coast of Argentina. Many other groups and areas could be named but it should also be observed that in some regions it is almost absent. Most of the North American Plains tribes rejected it, little has been found in Brazilian Amazonia, or in the extreme south of the continent. Variations in the type of deformity are related to both cultural and geographical differences. In the highlands of Peru and Bolivia the skulls are chiefly annular— the so-called 'Aymara' type; in the Mochica area the flat-vertical form is more common; in the Humahuaca territory almost all are flat-oblique. During excavations in this region a child's grave was discovered which contained a well-preserved example of the board and strapping apparatus, and anthropomorphic vases have been found at Lambayeque and elsewhere which show mothers applying the mechanism to their babies' heads. The efficiency of these various devices is

Plate 83

Plate 88

Fig. 33

well shown by a skull from Guatemala in which the cranial index is 123—in other words the compression of the head has reduced its length to only four-fifths of its breadth. An early traveller who saw head-moulding being applied to a baby in the Columbia River area of Canada draws a vivid picture of the operation. He says of the child, 'Its little black eyes, forced out by the tightness of the bandages, resembled those of a mouse choked in a trap.' And it is known that Chinook children whose heads were normally strapped to boards for two or three years sometimes died under the pressure.

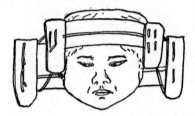

Fig. 33. Child wearing a head-moulding apparatus. Argentina.

The antiquity of this custom in America is uncertain but clearly varied from place to place. It is found at a very early date on Maya sites where, as is the case throughout most of the continent, it seems to be related to high rank. At Paracas in Peru, where large quantities of these skulls have been found, the oldest ones are deformed; from Cuba undeformed Ciboney skulls appear to ante-date deformed Arawak and Carib specimens.

Inevitably the question arises: what was the effect on the brain and intelligence? Did this tampering with nature lead to pathological changes? This is not easily answered for extinct populations. Despite the hot assertions of those who objected to the custom on aesthetic or other grounds, recent experience in western Europe has produced no really convincing evidence that the brain was injured or the mind impaired. Even where head-moulding is more pronounced, as in Sumatra, Malekula or Mangbetu, the brain seems plastic enough to adapt itself unharmed to the changing pattern of its coffer. It is the extreme distortions of the New World which excite suspicion. We know from early records that infants occasionally died from too savage binding of their heads: what of those who survived? The bi-lobed, almost kidney-shaped skulls of some ancient Peruvians or the high-pressed heads, like rostro-carinate flints, of Pueblo dwellers are so gross that despite the extraordinary ability of the human brain to adapt itself to a freakish tenement its functions must surely have been damaged at times. But if the psychopathological problem must remain a matter for conjecture, there is no doubt that on the physical side abnormal conditions were induced. Deflected nasal septa with partial obstruction of the airway and a tendency to sinusitis are found as well as inflammatory and degenerative changes in the wall of the skull.

Mutilation of the teeth is another custom which is found in many parts of the world and is of great antiquity. Three principal types occur: removal, filing and inlaying. In isolated cases it may be difficult to decide whether a tooth has been ritually ablated or whether its loss was due to accident or primitive dentistry; but usually the distinction is clear enough, and where many examples occur the constant pattern of ceremonial removal betrays its nature. The custom was already being practised in the Palaeolithic period. In the massive, craggy-headed Afalou bou Rhummel people, whose Oranian culture is a local North African variant of Capsian, one or more of the upper incisors are regularly knocked out. The Asselar man had suffered the same operation. This specimen is not precisely dated but it belongs to a time when a rich fauna and flora thronged the banks of a great tributary of the Niger in what is now the arid desert of the southern Sahara. The palaeolithic skulls from Shubka, Palestine, had been dealt with in the same fashion.

The easiest way to knock out a tooth is to strike directly at it using a hammer stone, with or without an interposed piece of wood to act as a punch. Instead of this, many groups have chosen to remove them by a forward pull or jerk in such a way that the bony sockets are fractured on the outer surface. This is regularly seen in the many early Siberian and American jaws which have been subjected to extraction. Usually it is the incisors which are removed, sometimes the deep-rooted canines or even the premolars. The reasons for the operation can only be surmised but aesthetic notions, status symbolism and clan discrimination probably accounted for many examples. Support for this view is found in the different distribution patterns which are met for the custom. In the Neolithic Irkutsk population, as also in a Koniag group, it occurred only in males. In early Siberian Voguls and some Alaskan Indians it was limited to females. Among Buriats 38 per cent of the women but only 7 per cent of the men showed ritual loss of teeth; in pre-Aleuts half the men and a third of the women had had the operation. It can hardly have been a prerogative of nobility when such a high proportion of the population carried the blazon, but in a series of nearly four thousand Peruvian skulls only one person in every twenty-five was so distinguished and here it may well have been the hall-mark of a patriciate or podestá. Cieza de León who was on the coast of Ecuador in the wake of Pizarro says definitely that tooth mutilation was practised by the caciques and nobility. The cranial evidence shows that the normal age for tooth ablation was during adolescence and this suggests a puberty initiation rite. In almost all groups the upper jaw is selected far more often than the lower.

Among the prehistoric Ainu tooth-removal is found in association with filing, a custom which is also widespread and may itself be associated with ornamental inlay. Space permits only a cursory glance at these procedures. Filing the biting edge

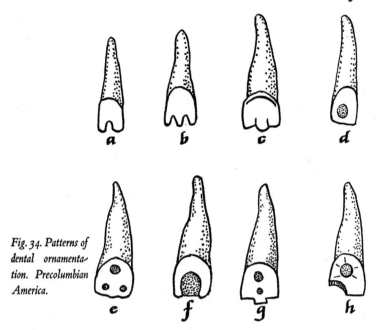

Fig. 34. Patterns of dental ornamentation. Precolumbian America.

of the teeth is by far the most usual method and many variations of it are met but the simple V-shaped notch or 'saw-edge' predominates. Many people have practised this custom in the Far East, Africa and the Americas. A much rarer type of filing is that of the Chamorros of Guam who cross-hatch the outer face of the upper incisors. Some of these deformities of the biting edge, especially those at the corners of teeth, are produced by chipping rather than filing. This is typical of African techniques and from there can be followed to Central and South America where the finest examples of inlay work are also found. Many different materials are used for inlaying. In Mexico, Guatemala and Yucatan green-stone, often referred to as jade or jadeite, was much favoured. Haematite and iron pyrites were also used and on rare occasions rock crystal. Gold inlays have been found in Ecuador at Atacames. In these

Fig. 34
Fig. 35

Fig. 35. Cross-hatch ornamentation of teeth. Chamorro.

171

places a brilliant standard of work was reached, above all in those teeth which have a combination of multiple tiny inlays with chipping and filing. Whether any kind of cement was used to retain the filling or whether pressure alone sufficed is uncertain. In some teeth which have shed their inlays a raised central point may be found at the bottom of the drilled cavity; this can only mean that some hollow instrument was used. If the pulp cavity was reached infection and decay inevitably followed, but these skilful dentists often removed only the enamel without broaching the underlying dentine. A superb piece of craftsmanship of this kind is seen in a woman's skull from La Piedra, Esmeraldas. Six upper teeth have had the enamel delicately erased and a gold overlay has been securely attached to each. By any standards of modern dentistry 'face crowning' of this excellence would be considered a difficult operation. These inlays seem always to have been inserted for aesthetic reasons, not to treat dental caries, but sometimes missing teeth were replaced. In one skull with gold inlay work from Atacames a lateral incisor had been implanted during life into a central incisor cavity which had lost its tooth. In a mandible from Copan, Honduras, a missing left lateral incisor had been replaced in the socket by a false one carved from brown stone. The incrustation of tartar showed that the tooth had been in use for some considerable period during the life of the patient. This triumph of dentistry from fifteen hundred years ago is one which even the Etruscan masters could not surpass, for they, when needing to replace lost teeth, did so in the modern manner with the artificial tooth carried on a gold band denture. These American inlays seem to be almost entirely confined to adults but filed teeth have been found in young people, as in the skull of a seven-year-old child from Sayate, north-west Argentina.

In addition to the skeletal evidence many anthropomorphic pots have been found which depict dental mutilation and the custom was obviously commonplace. On the other hand the fact that deities are often shown with inlaid teeth suggests that Plate 87 great importance was attached to the practice.

Few other types of artificial interference need detain us because few are recognized from early remains. Egyptian mummies have been found with their ears pierced for rings. Amputation of the fingers has been practised for ritual purposes among many modern primitives but ancient evidence of it is unconvincing. In Peru, at Hualla-Marca and Chancay, amputated feet, apparently of adolescent girls, have been discovered one of which was in an exceptionally elaborate mummy bundle with no other skeletal remains. It had been avulsed from the limb, so it could hardly represent an attempt to beautify the unfortunate subject of the mutilation. Amputated legs and arms are quite commonly shown in pottery from pre-columbian sites in this region. On Huaylas pottery amputated arms are represented as having been tattooed and bamboo tubes containing the powdered pigments for this operation have been recovered in Peruvian mummy packs. Primary evidence of tattooing can only be recognized where skin survives, and

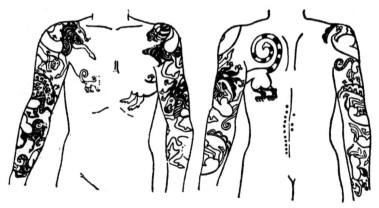

Fig. 36. Tattooings on the body of a chieftain. Pazirik. Fifth century B.C.

though it was probably a widely cherished adornment there is little direct evidence of it from the preliterate societies of antiquity. It has been found in natural sun-dried mummies of uncertain date from the Sudan but was not generally practised in ancient Egypt. Probably the finest of early tattooing is to be found in the frozen burials of the 'kindred Scythians' at

Fig. 36

Pazirik in the Altai. One man was embellished with intricate and beautiful animal motifs on his arms and trunk and the circumstances of his burial bear out the statements of Herodotus, Xenophon and Pomponius Mela who all describe tattooing as a sign of high rank. Secondary evidence for the custom is also found in neolithic pottery figurines from Butnir in Bosnia which show an elaborate form of punctate tattooing.

Male circumcision seems to be engraved on an Upper Palaeolithic baton from La Madeleine but the best testimony to the custom in antiquity comes from the abundant evidence of Egyptian mummies among which it was apparently universal in adult men. However, an eleven-year-old boy with shaved head but still wearing the Horus lock has been found uncircumcised, so it was probably a puberty rite. Bas-reliefs of the VI Dynasty from Sakkara show the operation in progress. In contrast to what is found today, female circumcision and infibulation seem never to have been customary in ancient Egypt and Nubia. Fresh or confirmatory evidence for mutilation can sometimes be found in the survival of early instruments used for performing the operation. A beautiful Romano-British castration clamp used in the rites of Cybele has been

Plate 86

dredged from the Thames near London Bridge; another, somewhat less ornate, was found near Basle.

Although the soft-tissue distortions which have survived from antiquity are scanty the range of these practices in modern peoples, sophisticated as well as primitive, assures us that many ancient groups must also have sought by cunning and contrivance the beauty which their bodies lacked by nature. It need cause no more surprise that a man should be entranced by the artificial shrinking of a woman's foot than that he should be allured by the kohl-dark pools around her eyes or the vibrating cascade of mascara on her lashes. Often our sensibilities are too narrow. We must always remember that if men and women have heard beauty in the plaint of Sappho's nightingales, they have seen it also in the turquoise inlays of Oaxacan teeth and no doubt caressed it, too, in the warm mystery of infibulation. And if at first the bi-lobed constriction of a Chinook skull seems too nightmarish a fantasy for our taste, we may yet find that by yielding it the sympathetic expectancy which we give to any other exotic form of art we may end by seeing a persuasive charm beyond its strangeness.

CHAPTER IX

Vital Statistics

*The World's a bubble and the life of man less
than a span.*

FRANCIS BACON

THE EVIDENCE OF DISEASE is twin-yoked to the age at death, and in reviewing morbidity we are drawn on to consider mortality. Unfortunately few problems are more slippery to solve than the estimation of a people's longevity and death rate from the surviving crumbs that are dug out of their burial grounds. But it is worth the attempt because these vital statistics goad the imagination and sharpen our understanding of what it meant to be an ancient Nubian or a mesolithic hunter.

The Neandertals, though far from being a homogeneous group, provide the first modest series for assessing the age at which they died: only one in twenty lived beyond the age of forty; eighty per cent perished before they were thirty. The Cro-Magnon upper palaeolithics fared little better. Even as late as the Anglo-Saxon period, when longevity had increased slightly but significantly in the first four decades of life, the number of persons reaching the age of fifty was still pathetically small. Figure 37 unfolds a bleak view of ancient societies in which the ripe benison of old age, as we know it today, was a gift that the gods bestowed but rarely.

Fig. 37

These figures must not be taken as more than approxima-tions, nor are they precisely comparable for the different popula-tions. The proportion of infant burials that are recovered fluctuates from one site to another depending on soil erosion, the time that has elapsed since inhumation and the method, meticulous or perfunctory, by which it was carried out. But

Group	Percentage of persons dead by the age of		
	30	40	50
Neandertals	80·0	95·0	100·0
'Cro-Magnons'	61·7	88·2	90·0
Mesolithics	86·3	95·5	97·0
Tepe Hissar	48·3	78·9	99·3
Caister Anglo-Saxons	57·4	81·8	97·5

Fig. 37. Proportion of deaths at different ages

the over-all picture is clear and it is repeated in countless early cemeteries. In nearly six hundred interments at Olynthos, Macedonia, half of them were children, mostly jar burials (*enchytrismoi*). A better group is that of more than a thousand pre-white Hawaiians on Oahu, yet even here almost a third died before attaining maturity and the average age at death for the *adults* was only thirty-one years.

Not all estimates give these very low figures. At the fifth- to sixth-century Frankish cemetery of Ennery a mean duration of life approaching forty years was calculated and it was specific-ally noted that this was a peaceful population where the deaths were due to natural causes. By the Middle Ages, despite the universal lack of hygiene, a gradual increase of longevity occurred in people who survived the diseases of infancy. Apart from its psychological value there is little advantage, in Western societies today, in breast-feeding babies; innumer-able children have been reared to perfect health on dried or canned milks. It is hardly too much to say that until recent times a bottle-fed baby was a dead baby, and in Egypt, Greece and Rome mothers who were unable to feed their children spent much care on choosing a suitable wet nurse in their stead. Unpasteurized cow's milk was the perfect medium for incubating the germs of dysentery and enteritis; it provided a constant focus from which these fatal diseases remained endemic in the child population of all countries. The infant mortality under such conditions was enormous, but if we disregard it and consider only those persons who survived to adolescence their subsequent fate, using the tenth- to twelfth-century population of Halimba-Cseres as a model, is shown in Figure 38. This shows the number of persons surviving at any subsequent year out of every 100 alive at the age of fifteen years.

Fig. 38

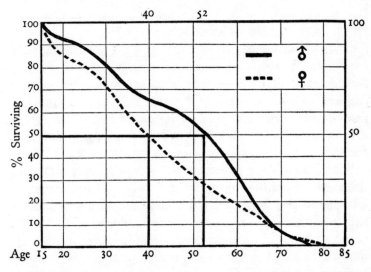

Fig. 38. Graph: Male and female survival rates.

It will be seen that there is a difference between the sexes. Wherever adequate numbers of old burials have survived the women are found to die younger that the men. Figure 39 illustrates this for several groups.

Fig. 39

The reason for the lower mean age of female deaths is uncertain but the trend began before maturity was reached. In the Texan group the sex ratio is already 112·6 males to 100

Group	Mean age at death of all adults who have attained an age of 18 years	
	Male	Female
Chalcolithic Anatolians	35·8	27·9
Norfolk Anglo-Saxons	38·1	30·4
Early Texas Indians	41·0	33·9
Ancient Romans	33·4	28·6
Aebelholt Medieval	34·0	27·7
Modern British	70·3	75·6

Fig. 39. Mean age at death

females by the age of eighteen years. Obstetric failures must account for some of the casualties and skeletons with a full-term foetus in the pelvis have been found at Villánykővesd, Hungary, Aebelholt, and elsewhere. In many societies the low status of women was probably even more important.

When a large series of burials can be reliably sexed, aged and dated we can estimate changes in the size of the community. The steady increase of the Halimba-Cseres population over five archaeological periods is shown in Figure 40. The infant mortality here was high, but unless the village grew by immigration, which is unlikely, the birth rate was keeping constantly ahead of the death rate by a slender margin. Amongst the Anglo-Saxons at Caister-on-Sea this did not happen; birth and death rates were balanced to give a steady population throughout their sojourn there. These were the people in whom radiography showed unusually many Harris's lines, with the implication of a generally high morbidity. It would appear that they were just able to withstand the stress of their environment but never achieved a good enough level of health and vigour to make themselves masters of it. The

Fig. 40

Period	Date	Size of Community
I	900– 960	83·8
II	960–1010	108·9
III	1010–1050	160·7
IV	1050–1100	193·2
V	1100–1120	239·5

Fig. 40. Population increase at Halimba-Cseres

Fig. 41

pattern of rise and fall through a thousand years of occupation at Pecos Pueblo is shown in Figure 41.

Attempts have been made to derive vital statistics from historical records. The fecundity of Macedonian, Seleucid and Ptolemaic queens has been calculated from what is known about their children. In all, thirty-four of these women produced sixty-one sons and, presumably, a roughly similar number of daughters. This gives a fertility rate of about 3·6

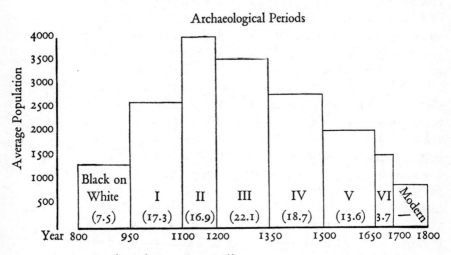

Fig. 41. Histogram: Population changes at Pecos Pueblo.

live births per woman. Close inbreeding was practised by many Near Eastern nations and six of these Ptolemies were married to their brothers. Careful study lends no support to the idea that the vitality or biological efficiency of themselves or their children was in any way impaired as a result.

From ancient Rome and the provinces of Hispania and Lusitania, and of Africa, thousands of sepulchral inscriptions survive which often give the age at death to the nearest day or hour, doubtless for astrological reasons. For both sexes the expectation of life in the provinces is much higher than in Rome, especially during the years of childhood, and in each area men have better prospects than women for all ages up to seventy-five. Sometimes the cause of death is given—pestis, gladio percussus, jugulatus, a tauru deceptus. The tombstone of a boy who died at four years and thirteen days has a sour reference to the astrologer who predicted a long life for him: 'Non igitur, lector, lachrimes: (de)cepit utrosque Maxima mendacis fama mathematici.' Studies in vital statistics of this kind give a dynamic view of the biological and ecological efficiency of whole groups. In prehistoric populations they may reveal unsuspected facts, for later periods they give interesting glosses on the historical record. Unfortunately few of these studies have been made.

One more factor in influencing the size of a population should be mentioned: deliberate control. Many primitive people are skilled in the use of contraceptives. The ancient Egyptians and Greeks used ingenious devices of woven voile steeped in salves or wax to occlude the opening into the uterus. Deformed or puny infants were left to die on the mountains or the sea-shore, but the hundred and seventy-five new-born babies excavated from a single well in Athens may have been abandoned during the siege of Sulla rather than the casual throw-outs of normal times. Finally, unwanted pregnancies were terminated by legalized abortion, and Hippocrates tells how a little singer and call-girl, all the rage with the bed-hoppers of the town, was dismayed to find herself enceinte since it would much reduce the price she could command. She sought his advice and he advised her 'to leap up and down, heels to arse'; she did so and the embryo 'fell to the ground with a plop'.

Historical Characters

There be of them, that have left a name behind them.

ECCLESIASTICUS

Fᴿᴏᴍ ᴇɢʏᴘᴛɪᴀɴ ᴍᴀsᴛᴀʙᴀ ᴛᴏᴍʙs, Mycenaean tholoi, neolithic barrows, Saxon urnfields and artless burial grounds in all continents the trowel of the excavator has reaped the bones or ashes of innumerable men and women. Men and women who once raised grateful faces to the warming sun or nuzzled chin down against the driven razor teeth of a Samhain sleet; anonymous thousands who once loved and hated, laughed and wept and were proud. From all those nameless hordes it sometimes happens that a known individual is lifted from his sepulchre to lie before us. The heightened interest of such a discovery grows in proportion to the historical significance or idiosyncrasy of the characters, and to examine them is a fascinating task for the anthropologist. We have already referred to several known persons: Tamerlaine, Swedenborg, and the pharaohs Siptah and Akhenaten. But the status of individuals who emerge name-clad and unique from the faceless anonymity of their fellows varies greatly. At times their identity is beyond dispute, as Napoleon's would be were his sarcophagus to be opened today. Often there is a measure of uncertainty and the examiner seeks to confirm an attribution rather than take it for granted. The case of Canute and his wife Queen Emma of Denmark who lie in uncivil neglect and mingled disarray with others in Winchester Cathedral would fall in this category if ever the authorities there should permit an enlightened reopening of their tomb. Because of the interest and importance of these autopsies we shall briefly consider a very few examples.

That post-mortem examinations may be directed to many different ends is well shown by the case of Lenin. After his death the Kremlin oligarchs hired a tame and famous neurologist to anatomize his brain. The investigation revealed that down to the minutest part its fibres, cells and nuclei were bigger and better, more complex and more noble, than those of other men. Today anyone who is interested—and reliably indoctrinated—can inspect under armed surveillance the thirty thousand serially labelled microscopic sections which disclose with materialistic infallibility the basis of Lenin's spiritual and intellectual supremacy. Such a *tour de force* is not for the common scientist to achieve. Usually the problem is a humdrum one of establishing the age, sex or pathology of our subject.

Ulrich von Hutten (d. 1523) illustrates this point. He was buried at Ufenau, Switzerland, where his alleged remains have recently been disinterred. The inscription on the tombstone says it is Hutten, the skeleton fits his known age of thirty-six years, the skull accords well with the two surviving woodcuts which portray him, and a rough area of osteitis on the left cheek bone tallies with a wound he is known to have received on that side of his face. Only one thing weighs against the attribution: Hutten claimed that he had syphilis and he left a detailed account of his disease and his eventual success in curing it with guaiac wood. No trace of this condition is present in the bones and though many syphilitics escape without skeletal changes Hutten's description of his symptoms would lead us to expect some osseous damage. A fleck of doubt thus tarnishes an otherwise convincing identification.

A different situation was presented by some bones that had been discovered in the Tower of London in 1674 and on the order of Charles II transferred to an urn in Westminster Abbey. Could they be, as Charles believed, the 'Princes in the Tower', one of whom was, of course, the lawfully reigning

King of England, the other his younger brother? The urn was opened in 1933 and its contents scrupulously examined: it was found to contain two children. Edward V was aged twelve years and nine months at the time of his death; Richard, Duke of York, was a few days short of his tenth birthday. Nothing is known of their physical appearance and the problem centred on a determination of the age of each skeleton, with the additional possibility that signs of violence might be found. The two bodies were estimated to be the exact age required by the historical record and the elder had an extensive brown stain over most of his face. There is little doubt that this was extravasated blood, typical of death by suffocation from pressure on the face. The traditional account of their death relates that they were 'smored and stifled' with feather pillows stuffed into their mouths, after which the murderers were instructed 'to burye them at the stayre foote, metely depe in the grounde', exactly where they were discovered in the White Tower in 1674. An unexpected finding was evidence of consanguinity between the two children. They both had wormian bones of unusual size and identical shape between their cranial sutures and both showed congenital suppression of some of their teeth. We have, then, good reason to suppose that these pathetic relics of mortality are indeed the last physical link with that high summer tragedy of five hundred years ago.

Fig. 5

No doubts clouded the identity of Robert the Bruce, King of Scotland, when his vault was opened in 1819, but a point of interest was raised by an old tradition that he died of leprosy. The skull did in fact show a pathological absence of his front teeth but Robert Liston, a surgeon of great eminence who examined it, thought this was due to fracture. A cast was taken before the bones were re-interred and it now seems likely, though perhaps not absolutely certain, that he was a leper. His breast bone was equally interesting as it had been sawn through longitudinally. This gave further proof that it was

Bruce's body because it is chronicled that before he died he ordered his heart to be taken from his breast and carried by Douglas to the Holy Sepulchre.

Far more doubtful were the alleged remains of Saint Magnus who was killed in A.D. 1115 and buried in the cathedral of his dedication at Kirkwall. The *Orkneyinga Saga* says that Lifolf, the executioner, hewed him two blows to kill him; the exhumed, decapitated skull had indeed been riven by a severe, perhaps fatal, gash on the dome and further injuries had damaged the base. This conformity between saga and lesions inspires confidence that the attribution is correct.

These scanty examples must suffice to show the type of problem this material presents.

Many another known person has survived the nibbling centuries to lie, all passion spent, in naked revelation beneath the anatomist's gaze. From the XI Dynasty princess Henhenit to Lorenzo the Magnificent, from Giuliano dei Medici to Alexander Pope the cadavers follow each other on the dissecting bench. Many display the wounds that cut them down, the ills that chafed their bodies and racked their sinews. Sooner or later to all of them, to each, the hemlock came; and touching these dusty fragments is to be reminded that our own descent into the shades is but an eye-blink away. Let us therefore, however cold and scientific our enquiry, handle these relics with awe and with compassion and let us, like the poet, remember that

> This quiet dust was gentlemen and ladies
>   and lads and girls;
> Was laughter and ability and sighing,
>   And frocks and curls.

Notes on the Figures

1 The left foot of the Pharaoh Siptah, XIX Dynasty. This is a form of 'club-foot' known as talipes equino-varus. It may arise from a congenital deformity or develop during childhood as a result of various pathological conditions. The shrinkage and shortening of the paralysed leg in polio-myelitis may be almost indistinguishable from primary orthopaedic defects of this kind. (Cf. Plate 44.)

2 Schematic drawing of a Peruvian mummy pack. The trussed body is surrounded by many layers of fine, coloured cotton fabrics often separated by layers of reed netting. The bundle is packed out with cotton floss and a false head of the same material surmounts the pack. This 'head' has imitation hair of agave fibre and a painted face with a wooden nose. (See small figure.) The mummy, wrapped in a *cushma*, may be wearing bracelets or other jewelry and a bag of chewing coca often accompanies it.

3 Rock painting from Jabbaren, Central Sahara. H. 34 cm. A series of these slender, seemingly emaciated figures is found in this locality. They bear no more relation to reality than the attenuated nymphs in the pages of modern fashion 'glossies' but they serve to illustrate in an extreme form one of the many varieties of 'pseudo-pathology' which are constant pitfalls when disease is diagnosed from art.

4 Negative imprints of human hands from the cave of Gargas, Haute-Garonne. Upper Palaeolithic. Various combinations of finger amputation are found.

5 Vault of skull. Two inter-sutural (wormian) bones are shown, one in the posterior part of the sagittal suture between the parietal bones and one in the left half of the lambdoid suture between the left parietal and the occipital bone. The frontal bone is divided into right and left halves by a metopic suture. This is constant in infancy but it is normally obliterated during childhood. The wormian bones and the metopism are both genetically determined.

6   Distal end of an Anglo-Saxon humerus. A supracondylar process springs from its antero-medial surface. This is a congenital atavistic anomaly; it represents part of the wall of a bony canal which is a normal feature in the carnivora and some other animals.

7   A bifid rib. Anglo-Saxon. This anomaly is genetically determined and may hint at consanguinity if it occurs with exceptional frequency in any group.

8   Steatite female figurine. Barma Grande cave, Grimaldi. Aurignacian, *c.* 25–30,000 B.C. H. 6·2 cm. The massive buttocks and protruding abdomen of this 'Venus' appear, when first seen, to be a caricature or symbolic exaggeration of femininity. The comparison with the figure of a modern female Bushman suggests that a steatopygous rump may have been normal in some of the upper palaeolithic peoples. Musée de Saint-Germain.

9   Stone star-headed mace. Peruvian, *c.* A.D. 1400. The weapon was hafted on a wooden handle and when brought down on an opponent's head produced a characteristic pair of depressed fractures, with radiating stellate fissures around them. Diameter of mace 9·2 cm. Lima, Museo Nacional.

10 Pott's fracture of the right leg. The fibula is broken at the junction of the middle and distal thirds; the medial malleolus at the distal extremity of the tibia is often, but not always, avulsed. This fracture is typically produced by stumbling accidentally and twisting the foot on the leg.

11 Colles' fracture of the left forearm. This impacted fracture, which occurs about an inch proximal to the wrist joint, is typical of a fall on to an outstretched hand. Note that the styloid process at the extreme tip of the ulna is also characteristically avulsed.

12 Fracture at the junction of the middle and distal thirds of the left ulna. This is the typical 'parry' fracture, sustained in guarding the head from a descending blow from a right-handed aggressor.

13 Articular condyle of the mandible. The figure on the left is normal with a smoothly rounded surface covered, in life, with cartilage. The right-hand figure shows advanced osteoarthritis in an Early Saxon. Degeneration and erosion of the cartilage has taken place, the underlying bone has also been worn down, its surface is irregular from osseous reaction and a jagged edge of bony 'lipping' projects round the margin of the re-fashioned condyle. Compensatory changes of a similar nature are found in the opposing face of the joint—the glenoid fossa of the temporal bone.

14 Wooden helmet in the form of a man's head. Tlingit. Probably nineteenth century. This is a realistic portrayal of a man with paralysis of the left side of his face. The likeliest cause of this would be a cerebral 'stroke' or hemiplegia due to senile arterial disease. It could, however, result from peripheral injury of the facial nerve, from mastoid disease or a lesion of variable cause known as Bell's paralysis. New York, American Museum of Natural History E/3453.

15 Proximal half of the left femur of *Pithecanthropus erectus*, the Java ape-man. Found 1892 in the Trinil beds of the Solo river, Java. *c.* 400,000 BP. The craggy mass of bone on the upper part of the shaft is an exostosis which probably developed from extravasated blood in a damaged muscle being organized into osseous tissue. This is quite distinct from the neo-plastic formation of bone that occurs in sarcoma. Leyden, Natural History Museum.

16 Distal end of a right tibia affected by osteomyelitis. The surface is roughened, with irregular thickening and pits; pus in the marrow cavity has discharged from several sinuses in the bone. Through the largest of these openings a detached piece of bone (a sequestrum) can be seen.

17 The tsetse fly *Glossina morsitans* is the vector which spreads the trypano-some of sleeping sickness (*ngana*). In recent centuries this disease has caused vast epizootics in Africa but the presence of the tsetse fly has been established in deposits of Oligocene date in Colorado, where trypano-somiasis may have eliminated the horses which inhabited America at that time. Scale about $\times 3\frac{1}{2}$.

18 Female pelvis from northern China. The distortion is due to osteo-malacia, an adult form of rickets in which the loss of calcium from the bones leads to their becoming soft and pliable. On vaginal examination in extreme cases it may be possible to introduce no more than one finger into the collapsed pelvic cavity.

19 Graphs showing dental caries rates from Neolithic times to the present for Britain, Denmark, France and Greece.

20 Molar teeth from the left side of lower jaw. Male aged 24 ± 2 years. Frankish. The first tooth to erupt, at the age of six years, is already severely eroded; the crown enamel is worn away exposing the dentine and the surface of the tooth is concave. The second molar, erupting at the age of twelve, has marked attrition of the cusps with exposure of the dentine starting in several places. The third molar, with six years less wear than the second and twelve years less than the first, still retains its cusp pattern, with negligible traces of crown wear.

21 Two right fifth metatarsal bones. 'A' is normal; 'B' shows an exag-gerated curvature due to external pressure from a tight sandal thong or some similar constriction.

22 Distal end of tibiae showing the articular surface of the ankle joint. In 'A' the anterior margin of the joint is sharp and unbroken. In 'B' the anterior edge is broken in its lateral half by an upturned extension of the articular area on to the anterior face of the bone. This is a typical squatting facet. In extreme dorsiflexion of the joint this facet comes into contact with a conterpart on the neck of the talus (astragalus). 'A' is English twelfth century or later; 'B' is English Bronze Age from Crichel, Dorset.

23 Transverse sections through the proximal thirds of (1) femora and (2) tibiae. (A) is stenomeric, (C) is eurycnemic—both are typical modern French. (B) is a platymeric Anglo-Saxon femur from Beckford, Gloucestershire; (D) is a platycnemic tibia of Neolithic date from Epône, Seine-et-Oise.

24 The right humerus of a Balearic slinger. *c.* 100 B.C. The prominent ridges in mid-shaft give insertion to the deltoid muscle which lifts and partly rotates the arm. The powerful traction exerted by this muscle has led to the bone yielding, in a marked lateral curvature, to its pull. Contrast the almost straight shaft of a normal humerus.

25 The distal end of a right humerus and proximal end of a right ulna. The anomalous perforation in the humerus is an epitrochlear foramen. Congenital in origin, it may be modified by impact with the olecranon (A) and coronoid (B) processes of the ulna.

26 A disc of parietal bone excised by trephining a neolithic skull. Lozère. Diam. 3·7 cm. Rondelles of this type are often perforated, as here, to serve as amulets or ornaments. Paris, Musée de l'Homme, Prunières collection.

27 Square trephination produced by sawing. Lachish, Israel. Iron Age *c.* 600 B.C. No sign of healing is present. London, British Museum (Natural History), 1944. 10.20.115.

28 Sincipital-T cauterization of the skull. Mantes, Seine-et-Oise. Neolithic. The long arm of the T starts in the mid-frontal region and extends back across the parietals. Note the partial interruption of scarring in the long limb.

29 Mid-shaft section of thigh bone. 'A' is that of a mountain pastoralist from Anatolia. Vigorous ranging over steep hill-sides imposes a great stress on the limbs, the cortex of the bone thickens to take the strain and the marrow cavity is reduced to a quarter of the diameter of the shaft. 'B' is from an elderly woman buried in conventual precincts in flat country, at Shouldham, Norfolk (*c.* twelfth–fourteenth century). The cortex of the bone is reduced to a thin shell and the marrow cavity occupies three-quarters of the total diameter. Spontaneous fracture may easily result from turning over in bed or the mere effort of standing when a bone such as this progresses to an advanced degree of osteoporosis.

30 Graph showing childhood morbidity rates in two Anglo-Saxon

populations: Burgh Castle and Caister-on-Sea. Although these groups were close contemporaries, living only five miles apart, their patterns of disease are very different.

31 This table shows the difference in age distribution of disease between the boys and the girls of an Anglo-Saxon village at Caister-on-Sea, Norfolk.

32 Head of a princess. Egyptian, XVIII Dynasty, *c.* 1365 B.C. This is a daughter of Nefertiti, perhaps by her husband Akhenaten, possibly by her father-in-law Amenhotep III. The long head is not due to artificial deformation. It is nothing more than an artistic convention of the el Amarna style. Egypt, Cairo Museum.

33 Head moulding apparatus. Humahuaca, Argentina. It consists of supple wooden boards applied to the front and back of the skull, on which the pressure can be adjusted by means of thongs at each side.

34 Dental mutilation. a, b and c are produced by filing; d, e and f are varieties of inlay; g and h are combinations of chipping and drilled inlays. Mexico and Ecuador.

35 Dental mutilation. Chamorro, Guam. Cross-hatch filing on the labial surface.

36 Tattooing on the body of the 'kindred Scythian' chieftain from Mound 2, Pazirik. Fifth century B.C.

37 This table shows the percentage of individuals dead by the ages 30, 40 and 50 in five early groups of people.

38 This graph shows the consistently higher survival rate of males as compared with females throughout adult life at the medieval site of Halimba-Cseres. Only in extreme old age is the position reversed.

39 This table shows the mean age at death of all adults who survive to eighteen years of age or more in five early populations. Females consis-

tently die younger than males. Only in modern times is this difference reversed.

40 This table shows how an approximately steady increase of the Halimba-Cseres population led to the size of the community being trebled over two and a quarter centuries.

41 This shows the rise and fall in the Pecos Pueblo community over a thousand years. The period of decline was about twice as long as the expansion phase.

Glossary of words as used in this book

Achondroplasia. A form of dwarfism in which the limbs are greatly shortened but the trunk is almost normal.

Acromegaly. A disease of the pituitary gland which leads to excessive growth of the face, hands and feet.

Actinomycosis. Infection of bones or other tissues by the 'ray' fungus.

Albinism. The state of being a congenital albino.

Alkaptonuria. A congenital metabolic condition in which the urine turns black soon after it has been passed.

Alveolus. The tooth-bearing margin of a jaw.

Ankylosis. Fusion of the bones at a joint.

Antrum. The maxillary sinus, an air-containing cavity in the upper jaw.

Aorta. The main artery coming from the heart; it ends at the level of the fourth lumbar vertebra by dividing into the common iliac arteries.

Apical abscess. An abscess round the tip of a tooth root.

Arteriosclerosis. Thickening and hardening of the walls of arteries.

Bartonellosis. Infection by *Bartonella bacilliformis* causing the disease variously known as verruga peruana, Oroya fever or Carrión's disease.

Basal celled carcinoma. Rodent ulcer, a relatively benign form of skin cancer.

Bejel. A non-venereal form of syphilis.

Beri-beri. A disease due to lack of thiamin (vitamin B_1).

Bilharzia. Schistosomiasis, a disease due to trematode worms which live in the blood vessels.

Blastomycetes. Fungi allied to the yeasts.

Boomerang leg. Abnormal curving of the leg bones, possibly due to yaws.

Callus. Excess bone produced in the repair of fractures.

Carcinoma. Cancers which begin in skin, mucous membranes or glands.

Chimney sweeps' cancer. Carcinoma of the scrotum.

Chlorosis. A form of anaemia which was usually seen in adolescent girls.

Colles' fracture. A fracture of the radius immediately proximal to the wrist.

Cor bovinum. 'Ox heart', the greatly enlarged heart typical of chronic heart failure.

Cretin. A dwarf due to thyroid insufficiency.

Cribra orbitalia. A sieve-like appearance in the roof of the eye socket, of uncertain cause.

Cushing's disease. An endocrine disease associated with obesity and excessive growth of hair.

Diaphysis. The main part of the shaft of long bones.

Elephantiasis. A gross thickening of the soft tissues of the lower limbs and elsewhere, commonly due to infection by nematode worms of the Filariidae family.

Emphysema. Overstretching of the alveoli of the lungs, with destruction of their walls.

Epiphysis. The detached caps on the ends of bones from which growth takes place.

Ergotism. Poisoning due to ergot, the 'black smut fungus' of rye and other grain.

Espundia. The South American form of leishmaniasis, also called uta.

Exostosis. An abnormal, but non-malignant outgrowth of bone; often traumatic in origin.

Femur. The thigh bone.

Fibrosis. The conversion of any other tissue in the body into fibrous tissue.

Fibula. The lateral bone of the lower leg.

Filariasis. Infection by worms of the genus *Filaria*, a common cause of elephantiasis.

Fluorosis. Poisoning from excessive intake of fluorides.

Framboesia. Yaws, a disease due to *Treponema pertenue*.

Gangosa. A destruction of the tissues of the face due to yaws.

Gingivitis. Inflammation of the gums.

Goitre. Enlargement of the thyroid gland in the neck.

Graves' disease. A toxic condition due to abnormal activity of the thyroid gland.

Haematoma. A swelling due to a collection of blood, whether clotted or not.

Haemophilia. 'Bleeder's disease', a congenital disease in which the clotting powers of the blood are much reduced.

Harris's lines. Lines of increased calcification across the ends of long bones. They are due to interference with normal growth.

Hashimoto's disease. A form of goitre (or sometimes atrophy of the thyroid gland) due to the adverse effect of antibodies which have been evoked by the patient's own abnormal gland.

Hemiplegia. A unilateral paralysis (often with accompanying sensory changes) due to damage to the brain.

Hormone. A chemical secreted by a ductless gland and conveyed through, out the body by the blood stream.

Humerus. The bone of the upper arm.

Huntingdon's chorea. A congenital disease which appears in middle life or later; it somewhat resembles St Vitus's dance.

Hydatid disease. Infection by organisms of the genus *Echinococcus.* Large cysts containing the cestodes develop in the liver, lungs and other organs.

Hydrocephaly. Distension of the brain, and later of skull, by excess cerebro-spinal fluid in the ventricles of the brain.

Hydrocoele. A collection of fluid around a testicle.

Hysterectomy. Surgical removal of the uterus.

Impetigo. A crusted skin rash, commonly due to infection by staphylo, cocci.

Infibulation. A form of 'female circumcision'.

Juxta-articular swellings. Swellings near joints which are found in yaws, syphilis and a few other diseases.

Kachine-Beck disease. A form of poly-arthritis of unknown origin common in parts of Siberia.

Kinneir-Wilson disease. A congenital inability to excrete the minute amounts of copper which are ingested during life; it leads to a form of copper poisoning.

Klippel-Feil disease. A congenital deformity of the spine, ribs and adjacent structures.

Lambdoid suture. The cranial suture separating the occipital from the two parietal bones.

Leishmaniasis. A group of diseases caused by parasites of the genus *Leishmania*; it includes the Old World kala-azar and Aleppo sore and the American uta (q.v.).

Leontiasis ossea. A diffuse hypertrophy of the bones of the face and skull. Cause variable. Very rare.

Lichen. A chronic papular eruption of the skin.

Lues venerea. Syphilis (q.v.).

Lupus erythematosus. A skin disease due to auto-antibodies in the circulation appearing as a result of the breakdown of normal immunization mechanisms. Wholly distinct from lupus vulgaris which is a tuberculous skin infection.

Mastitis. Inflammation of the breast.

Melanoma. A highly malignant cancer, often starting in a deeply pigmented 'mole' on the skin.

Meningioma. A form of intracranial tumour.

Metastatic abscess. One carried in the blood or lymph vessels from a primary site; not developing by local extension of an existing infection.

Metopic suture. A midline suture dividing the frontal bone into two halves. Constant in children, usually absent in adults.

Mitral valve. A valve of the heart, separating the left auricle from the left ventricle.

Morbus gallicus. An early name for syphilis.

Myelomatosis. An uncommon form of malignant growth.

Neoplasm. Literally 'a new growth', usually applied to any form of cancer.

Neuritis. Inflammation of a nerve.

Oroya fever. Bartonellosis (q.v.).

Osteitis. Inflammation of a bone.

Osteochondritis. A form of injury of uncertain cause in which cartilage invades the bony surface of a joint.

Osteoma. A non-malignant bony growth.

Osteomalacia. Adult rickets due to severe calcium loss.

Osteophytosis. Craggy outgrowths of bone; often called 'lipping' when found on vertebrae or joints.

Paget's disease. A thickening of the bones of the skull, limbs and elsewhere. Of unknown cause.

Painter's colic. Due to chronic lead poisoning.

Palaeopathology. The study of pathological conditions in early peoples and other animals from non-literary sources.

Parietals. Two bones on the top of the head separated by the midline sagittal suture.

Pellagra. A disease due to deficiency of the nicotinic acid portion of the vitamin B complex.

Pericardium. The fibrous sac surrounding the heart.

Periostitis. Inflammation of the periosteum—the membrane covering the bones.

Perthes' disease. A degenerative condition affecting the hip joint.

Pinta. An American disease due to *Treponema carateum*; allied to syphilis and yaws.

Pituitary gland. An endocrine gland lying immediately below the brain. It has several dozen functions and largely controls the rest of the ductless glands.

Platycnemia. Side to side flattening of the shin bone.

Platymeria. Front to back flattening of the upper part of the thigh bone.

Polydactyly. Congenital supernumerary fingers or toes.

Pott's disease. Tuberculosis of the spine.

Pott's fracture. Fracture of the lower part of the fibula, often associated with a tibial fracture.

Psoriasis. A chronic scaly skin disease.

Radius. The outer bone of the forearm when the palm of the hand is uppermost.

Raynaud's disease. A familial condition in which spasm of the arteries leads to gangrene of the fingers and toes.

Relapsing fever. A group of Treponeme infections conveyed by lice or tick bites. Especially common in hot climates. Very distinct from the treponematoses of the syphilis⁄framboesia⁄pinta group.

Rhinophyma. A chronic thickening of the nose.

Rickettsial infections. Diseases due to organisms of this group; the most important is typhus which is caused by *Rickettsiae prowazeki.*

Rubella. German measles.

Sacrum. The lowest bone of the spinal series, apart from the coccyx. It is the posterior part of the pelvis.

Sagittal suture. The midline cranial suture separating the two parietal bones.

Saprophytes. Organisms which live on dead tissues.

Sarcoma. A cancer starting in bone.

Semilunar cartilages. Two cartilages attached to the head of the tibia inside the knee joint.

Sickle⁄cell anaemia. A blood disease especially common in Africans; red corpuscles of sickle shape are obtrusive in this condition.

Sincipital⁄T. A T⁄shaped lesion of the skull produced by cauterization.

Steatopygia. Big buttocks; characteristic of Bushmen.

Synovial membrane. The serous membrane lining joints and tendon sheaths.

Syphilis. Infection by *Treponema pallidum* (formerly *Spirochaeta pallida*). It occurs in venereal and non-venereal forms.

Tetanus. Lockjaw; due to *Clostridium tetani.*

Thyroid. An endocrine gland in the neck.

Tibia. The shin bone.

Trepanation. An opening made artificially in the vault of the skull; identical with trephination.

Trepenarid. Non-venereal syphilis.

Trephination. See Trepanation.

Ulna. The inner bone of the forearm when the palm of the hand is uppermost.

Urticaria. 'Nettle-rash', a group of skin diseases showing raised wheals, often allergic in origin.

Uta. American leishmaniasis: espundia.

Variola. Smallpox.

Verruga peruana. Bartonellosis (q.v.).

Wormian bones. Small, inconstant bones occurring in the sutures of the skull.

Yaws. Framboesia (q.v.).

Bibliography

In each section items are listed in chronological order. Inevitably there is occasional overlapping between the articles in different sections.

General

SMITH, G. E. and JONES, F.W. 1910. *Bull. Archaeol. Surv. Nubia.* Vol. 2, *The Human Remains.* Cairo. A pioneer study based on several thousand bodies.

RUFFER, M. A. 1921. *Studies in the Palaeopathology of Egypt* (ed. R. L. Moodie). Univ. Chicago Press. An excellent collection of miscellaneous papers.

MOODIE, R. L. 1923. *Paleopathology. An introduction to the study of ancient evidences of disease.* Urbana: Univ. Illinois Press. An important work. It deals with the palaeopathology of plants and animals as well as human material.

MACCURDY, G. G. 1923. Human skeletal remains from the highlands of Peru. *Am. J. Phys. Anthrop.*, 6: 217–329. A substantial contribution to the literature.

PALES, L. 1930. *Paléopathologie et pathologie comparative.* Paris: Masson. An excellent work with a bibliography of more than 650 items.

MOODIE, R. L. 1931. *Roentgenologic studies of Egyptian and Peruvian Mummies.* Field Mus. Nat. Hist. Anthrop. Mem., Vol. 3. Chicago. An early volume with many good radiographs.

ACKERKNECHT, E. H. 1953. Paleopathology, in *Anthropology To-day.* Univ. Chicago Press. A brief summary.

BABY, R. S. 1954. *Hopewell cremation practices.* Ohio Hist. Soc. Pap. in Archaeol., No. 1. A good example of what can be learned from cremated remains.

MØLLER-CHRISTENSEN, V. 1958. *Bogen om Aebelholt kloster.* Copenhagen. A meticulous study of disease in a medieval cemetery.

NEMESKÉRI, J. and HARSÁNYI, L. 1959. Die Bedeutung paläopathologischer Untersuchungen für die historische Anthropologie. *Homo,* 10: 203–26. A good review of some medieval burial sites in Eastern Europe.

RONEY, J. G. 1959. Palaeopathology of a California archaeological site. *Bull. Hist. Med.,* 33: 97–109. One small group studied in relation to its environment.

WELLS, CALVIN. 1960. A study of cremation. *Antiquity,* 34: 29–37. General and specific conclusions based on an Anglo-Saxon urn-field.

WATERMANN, R. 1960. Paläopathologische Beobachtungen am altägyptischen Skeletten und Mumien. *Homo,* 11: 167–79.

WELLS, CALVIN. 1961. A new approach to ancient disease. *Discovery,* 22: 526–31. First use of Harris's lines to assess childhood morbidity in ancient peoples.

SNOW, C. E. 1961. An old Hawaiian population on Oahu. *Proc. 30th ann. meeting Am. Assoc. Phys. Anthrop.* (Abstract in *Am. J. Phys. Anthrop.,* 20: 69–70.) An extensive review of over a thousand skeletons.

MOREL, P. and DEMETZ, J. L. 1961. *Pathologie osseuse du Haut Moyen-Age.* Paris: Masson. A useful study of medieval Burgundians.

BUGYI, B. 1961. Znaczenie Paleopatologii dla Antropologii. *Czlowiek,* 4: 4, 176–81. Discusses the importance of palaeopathology for anthropology.

SMITH, G. E. and DAWSON, W. R. 1924. *Egyptian mummies*. London: Allen and Unwin. A useful introduction for the non-specialist.

ROHEN, J. 1959. Histologische Untersuchungen an Augen altkanarischer Mumien. *Homo*, 10: 35–9. Deals with the microscopic study of mummy eyes.

SANDISON, A. T. 1963. In *Science and archaeology*, edited by D. Brothwell and E. S. Higgs. Chap. 40, 'The study of mummified and dried human tissues', 413–25.

WROZOSEK, A. 1960. O Mumifikacji zwlok Ludzkich. *Czlowiek*, 3: 1, 25–31. Describes a group of medieval mummies.

WAISBARD, R. and S. 1961. *La vie splendide des momies péruviennes.* Paris: Réné Julliard. Pleasantly readable.

Congenital

BARCLAY-SMITH, E. 1911. Multiple anomaly in a vertebral column. *J. Anat. Physiol.*, 45: 144–71. An interesting description and misdiagnosis: it is a case of Klippel-Feil deformation.

DAWSON, W. R. 1927. Dwarfs and hunchbacks in Ancient Egypt. *Ann. Med. Hist.*, 9: 315–26. Describes numerous examples—especially of achondroplasia.

HOHENTHAL, W. D. and BROOKS, S. T. 1960. An archaeological scaphocephal from California. *Am. J. Phys. Anthrop.*, 18: 59–67. Describes in detail an extreme example.

Injury

BLACK, D. 1925. The human skeletal remains from the Sha Kuo T'un cave deposit in comparison with those from Yang Shao Tsung and with North China skeletal material. *Palaeontologia Sinica*, Ser. D. Vol. I: fasc. 3. An intensive survey.

MOREL, C. and BAUDOUIN, M. 1928. Un cas intéressant de pathologie préhistorique. *Progrès médical*, No. 25. Describes flint arrow wounds.

INGELMARK, BO E. 1939. In THORDEMAN, B. *Armour from the battle of Wisby, 1361*. Uppsala. Chapter 4, 'Skeleton finds from the warrior graves outside Wisby'. A useful analysis of the battle injuries.

EHRHARDT, SOPHIE. 1960. Schlagspuren, Brüche und Sprünge an den Skeletten von Langhnaj im nördlichen Gujarat, Vorderindien. *Anthrop. Anz.*, 24: 2/3, 178–83. Contains a suggestion of cannibalism.

WELLS, CALVIN. 1961. A human skull from Runham, Norfolk. *Norfolk Archaeol.*, 32: 312–15. Describes a deformed Iron Age Briton who was decapitated perhaps because of mental abnormality.

Degenerations

LINDBLOM, K. 1951. Backache and its relation to ruptures of the inter-vertebral discs. *Radiology*, 57: No. 5, 710–19. Contrasts modern with ancient populations.

STRAUSS, W. L. and CAVE, A. J. E. 1957. Pathology and posture of Neanderthal man. *Quarterly Rev. Biol.*, 32: 348–63. Refutes the suggestion that *Homo neanderthalensis* did not walk erect.

DASTUGUE, J. 1958. Note de paléopathologie sur quatre 'blocs' bi-vertébraux. *Bull. Mém. Soc. Anthrop.*, 10ᵉ Sér., 9: 320–7. Describes examples of different bone disease.

INGLEMARK, BO E., MØLLER-CHRISTENSEN V. and BRINCH, O.

1959. Spinal joint changes and dental infections. *Acta Anatomica*, 38: Suppl. 36.

SANDISON, A. T. 1962. Degenerative vascular disease in the Egyptian mummy. *Med. Hist.*, 6: 77–81. A fine essay with brilliant micro-photographs.

New Growths

WILLIAMS, G. D., RITCHIE, W. A. and TITTERINGTON, P. F. 1941. Multiple bony lesions suggesting myeloma in precolumbian Indian aged ten years. *Am. J. Roentgenol.*, 46: 351–5.

OAKLEY, K. P. and TOBIAS, P. V. 1960. The Kanam jaw. *Nature*, 185: 945–7. Includes a comment on its tumour.

BÉRAUD, C., MOREL, P. and BOYER, ABBÉ R. 1961. Ostéome géant fronto-ethmoidal découvert sur un crâne médiéval du Var. *J. Radiol. Electrol.*, 42: 1/2, 45–7. Describes a freak case.

Non-specific infections

SANDISON, A. T. 1959. The first recorded case of inflammatory mastitis —Queen Atossa of Persia and the physician Democedes. *Med. Hist.*, 3: 317–22. A penetrating essay in diagnosis. (Many of the references in the 'General' section also discuss these conditions.)

Specific infections

ROBINSON, V. 1938. Did Columbus discover syphilis? *Brit. J. Dermat. Syphil.*, 50: 593–605. A discussion based on the historical, not the skeletal, evidence.

SALAMAN, R. N. 1939. Deformities and mutilations of the face as depicted in the Chimú pottery of Peru. *J. Roy. Anthrop. Inst.*, 69: 109–22. Thinks many of these were derived from the shape of potatoes.

CHALIAN, W. 1940. An essay on the history of lockjaw. *Bull. Hist. Med.*, 8: 171–201.

HOLCOMB, R. C. 1941. The antiquity of congenital syphilis. *Bull. Hist. Med.*, 10: 148–77. Extensive historical discussion: supports pre/columbian syphilis in the Old World only.

THORNDIKE, LYNN. 1942. A possible reference to syphilis before the discovery of America. *Bull. Hist. Med.*, 11: 474. Discusses a MS. in the Laurentian library, Florence.

SCOTT, H. H. 1943. The influence of the slave trade in the spread of tropical disease. *Trans. R. Soc. Trop. Med. Hyg.*, 37: 169–88. A useful reminder of some neglected facts.

JONCKHEERE, F. 1948. Le Bossu des Musées Royaux d'Art et d'Histoire de Bruxelles. *Chronique d'Égypt*, 23: 24–35. Describes an early Egyptian figurine of Pott's disease.

RITCHIE, W. A. 1952. Paleopathological evidence suggesting pre/columbian tuberculosis in New York State. *Am. J. Phys. Anthrop.*, 10: 305–17.

HARE, RONALD. 1954. *Pomp and pestilence. Infectious disease, its origins and conquest.* London: Gollancz. Brief, brilliant and highly readable.

HUDSON, E. H. 1958. *Non/venereal syphilis. A sociological and medical study of bejel.* Edinburgh: Livingstone. A useful introduction to an interesting disease.

MØLLER/CHRISTENSEN, V. 1961. *Bone changes in leprosy.* Copenhagen: Munksgaard. Contains early as well as modern material: an excellent study.

MOORE, D. 1961. Prehistoric tuberculosis in America. *Proc. 30th Ann. meeting Am. Assoc. Phys. Anthrop.* (Abstract in *Am. J. Phys. Anthrop.*, 20: 64.) Leaves its occurrence open to doubt.

Endocrine and Metabolic diseases

MARGETTS, E. L. 1951. The masculine character of Hatshepsut, Queen of Egypt. *Bull. Hist. Med.*, 25: 559–62.

ALDRED, CYRIL and SANDISON, A. T. 1962. The Pharaoh Akhenaten: a problem in Egyptology and Pathology. *Bull. Hist. Med.*, 36: 293–316. A first-rate discussion of a fascinating problem.

Deficiency diseases

GAN, J. K. 1945. Note sur un fémur humain rachitique d'un dolmen de l'Aveyron. *Bull. Mém. Soc. Anthrop.*, 9ᵉ Sér., 6: 63–70.

Dental diseases

LEIGH, R. W. 1930. Dental morphology and pathology of prehistoric Guam. *Mem. Bernice P. Bishop Mus.*, 11: 255–73.

CHRISTOPHERSON, K. M. 1939. Investigations into dental conditions in the Neolithic Period and in the Bronze Age in Denmark. *Dent. Rec.*, London, 59: 575–85.

WEINBERGER, B. W. 1948. *An introduction to the history of dentistry.* (2 vols.) St. Louis. Volume I contains much early material of great interest.

SOGNNAES, R. F. 1956. Histological evidence of developmental lesions in teeth originating from palaeolithic, prehistoric and ancient times. *Am. J. Path.*, 32: 547–77. A good study of the micro-anatomy of dental lesions.

CLEMENT, A. J. 1956. Caries in the South African ape-man: some examples of undoubted pathological authenticity believed to be 800,000 years old. *Brit. Dent. J.*, 101: 4–7.

HADJIMARKOS, D. M. and BONHORST, C. W. 1962. Fluoride and selenium levels in contemporary and Ancient Greek teeth in relation to dental caries. *Nature,* 193: 4811, 177–8.

MILES, A. E. W. 1962. Assessment of the ages of a population of Anglo-Saxons from their dentitions. *Proc. R. Soc. Med.,* 55: 881–6. An important new development in Vital Statistics.

Mental disorder

POSNANSKY, A. 1925. Die erotischen Keramiken der Mochicas und deren Beziehungen zu occipital deformierten Schädeln. *Abhandl. Anthrop. Ethnol. Urg.,* 2: 67–74.

SANDISON, A. T. 1958. The Madness of the Emperor Caligula. *Med. Hist.,* 2: 202–9. Thinks it was due to encephalitis.

Trephination

MUNIZ, M. A. and McGEE, W. J. 1897. Primitive trephining in Peru. *16th Ann. Rep. Bur. Amer. Ethnol., Washington.* A splendid pioneer work.

GUIARD, E. 1930. *La trépanation cranienne chez les néolithiques et chez les primitifs modernes.* Paris: Masson. A standard work with a bibliography of 242 items.

GRAÑA, F., ROCCA, E. D. and GRAÑA, L. R. 1954. *Las trepanaciones craneanas en el Perú en la época prehispánica.* Lima. A valuable study.

WERTHEIMER, P., AVET, J., LEVY, A. and JENOT, J. 1956. Les lacunes osseuses de la voûte cranienne. *Presse Médicale,* 68: 1556–9. Notes many conditions that can produce holes in the skull.

JANSSENS, P. A. 1959. Trépanations préhistoriques. *Bull. Soc. R.*

Belge Anthrop. Préhist., 70: 69–81. Emphasizes the conditions which may simulate trephination.

DASTUGUE, J. 1959. Un orifice cranien préhistorique. *Bull. Mém. Soc. Anthrop.*, 10ᵉ Sér., 10: 357–63. Important. It offers evidence that trephination was practised in Mesolithic times.

Artificial Interference

DELISLE, F. 1889. Les déformations artificielles du crâne en France. *Bull. Soc. Anthrop.*, 3ᵉ Sér., 12:649–69. Delisle made an extensive study of the custom whilst it was still widely practised.

DINGWALL, E. J. 1931. *Artificial cranial deformation.* London: Bale and Danielsson. Comprehensive: a standard work.

FALKENBERGER, F. 1938. Recherches anthropologiques sur la déformation artificielle du crâne. *J. Soc. Américanistes (Paris)*, 30: 1–70. An analysis of 300 South American specimens.

BORBOLLA, D. F. RUBIN DE LA. 1940. Types of tooth mutilation found in Mexico. *Am. J. Phys. Anthrop.*, 26: 349–62. A good account of this custom.

KURTH, G. 1958. Zur Stellung der neolithischen Menschenreste von Khirokitia auf Cypern. *Homo*, 9: 20–31. Produces evidence from the fourth millennium B.C.

Vital Statistics

MACDONELL, W. R. 1913. On the expectation of life in ancient Rome, and in the provinces of Hispania and Lusitania, and Africa. *Biometrika*, 9: 366–80. A study based wholly on sepulchral inscriptions.

VALLOIS, H. V. 1937. La durée de la vie chez l'Homme fossile.

L'Anthrop., 47: 499–532. Discusses most of the known Palaeolithic and Mesolithic specimens.

WEIDENREICH, F. 1939. Duration of life of fossil Man in China and pathological lesions found in his skeleton. *Chinese Med. J.*, 55: 34–44. A valuable paper now that the *Pithecanthropus sinensis* specimens are lost.

ANGEL, J. L. 1947. The length of life in Ancient Greece. *J. Geront.*, 2: 18–24. A good discussion based on skeletal remains.

GOLDSTEIN, M. S. 1953. Some vital statistics based on skeletal material. *Hum. Biol.*, 25: 3–12. With special reference to precolumbian Texas.

ACSADI, G. and NEMESKÉRI, J. 1957. Paläodemographische Probleme am Beispiel des fruhmittelalterlichen Gräberfeldes Halimba-Cseres Kom. Veszprém, Ungarn. *Homo*, 8: 133–48. An outstanding analysis of the Vital Statistics at a medieval site.

Miscellaneous

ESPER, E. J. C. 1774. *Ausfürliche Nachrichten von neuentdeckten Zoolithen unbekannter vierfüssiger Thiere.* Nuremburg. Perhaps the first palaeo-pathological specimen to be described.

DECKER, F. H. and BOHROD, M. G. 1939. Medullary artifacts in pre-historic bones. *Am. J. Roentgenol.*, 42: 374–5. Warns that soil conditions may simulate disease.

NAVARRO, J. M. DE. 1955. A doctor's grave of the Middle La Tène period from Bavaria. *Proc. Prehist. Soc.*, 21: 231–48. Describes the surgical instruments that were found.

MORGENTHALER, P. W. and BAUD, C. A. 1957. Sur une cause d'altération des structures dans l'os humain fossile. *Bull. Schweiz.*

Gesellsch. Anthrop. Ethnol., 33: 9–10. Warns that fungal invasion may simulate disease.

JANSSENS, P. A. 1957. Medical views on prehistoric representations of human hands. *Med. Hist.*, 1: 318–22. A judicious consideration of the mutilated handprints at Gargas.

GLOB, P. V. 1959. *Jernaldermanden fra Grauballe*. Århus. An account of the bog burial: a summary in English.

HENSCHEN, F. 1960. *Emanuel Swedenborg's cranium. A critical analysis.* Uppsala: Almqvist and Wiksells. A collaborative investigation of the two rival skulls.

HUG, E. 1960. Das fragliche Skelett des Ulrich von Hutten. *Bull. Schweiz. Gesellsch. Anthrop. Ethnol.*, 36: 34–46.

SMITH (now GLEMSER), MADELEINE. 1960. Blood groups of the ancient dead. *Science*, 131: No. 3402, 699–702. An excellent account by one of the pioneers of this important subject.

GLEMSER, M. S. 1963. In *Science and archaeology*, edited by D. Brothwell and E. S. Higgs. Chap. 42, 'Palaeoserology', 437–46.

WELLS, CALVIN. 1963. In *Science and archaeology*, edited by D. Brothwell and E. S. Higgs. Chap. 39, 'The radiological examination of human remains', 401–12.

Textual sources and historical studies

PAUL OF AEGINA. *The seven books of Paulus Aegineta.* Trans. F. Adams. 3 vols., London, 1844–6.

ARETAEUS. *The extant works of Aretaeus.* Ed. and trans. F. Adams. London, 1856. A readable translation of this important author.

MILNE, ST J. 1907. *Surgical instruments in Greek and Roman times.* Oxford.

HIPPOCRATES. Ed. and trans. by W. H. S. Jones and E. T. Withington. 4 vols. New York, 1923–31. (Loeb Classical Library.)

WONG, K. C. and WU, L. T. 1936. *History of Chinese medicine* (2nd ed.). Shanghai. An excellent introduction.

EBBELL, B. 1937. *The papyrus Ebers, the greatest Egyptian medical document.* London: O.U.P.

METTLER, C. C. 1947. *History of medicine.* Philadelphia: Blakiston Co. Packed with information despite its bad format.

SIGERIST, H. E. 1951–61. *A history of medicine.* Vol. 1, *Primitive and archaic medicine.* Vol. 2, *Early Greek, Hindu, and Persian medicine.* New York: O.U.P. A good general introduction.

GRATTAN, J. H. G. and SINGER, C. 1952. *Anglo-Saxon Magic and Medicine.* Oxford. Useful and readable.

RIESE, W. 1953. *The conception of disease. Its history, its versions and its nature.* New York: Philosophical Library. Provocatively interesting.

PENNACCHIA, T. 1960. *La storia della medicina Maya.* Pisa: Scientia Veterum.

OPPENHEIM, A. L. 1962. Mesopotamian medicine. *Bull. Hist. Med.,* 36: 97–108. A brief survey.

GHALIOUNGUI, P. 1963. *Magic and medical science in Ancient Egypt.* London: Hodder and Stoughton. A masterly review of the subject.

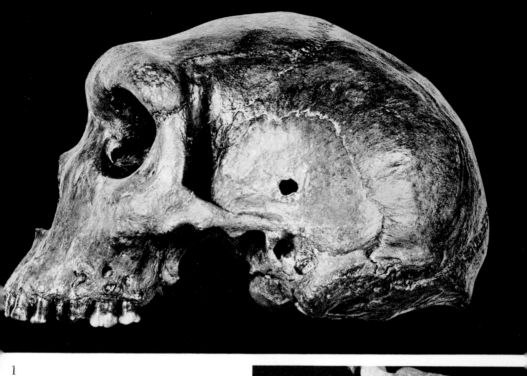

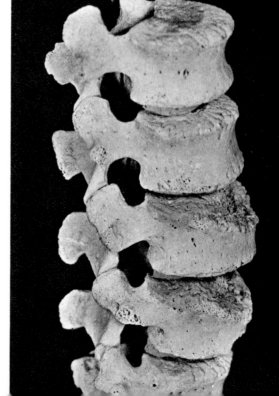

1

2

3

4

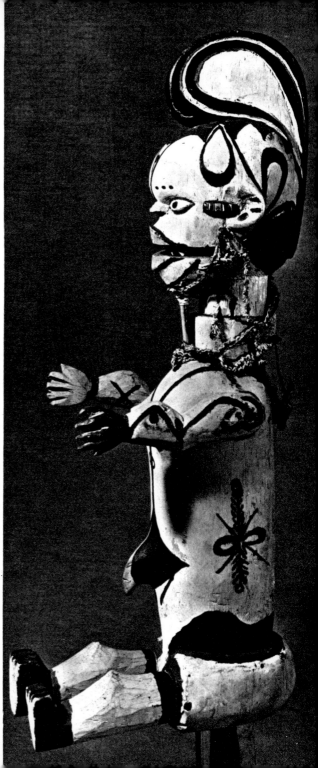

5

7

8

9

10

11

12

13

14

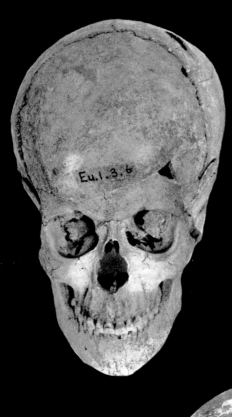

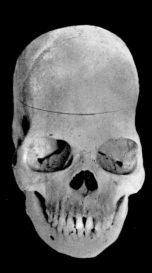

15

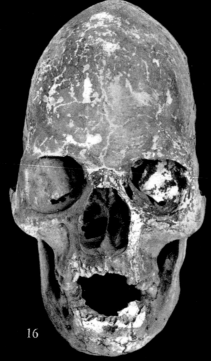

16

17

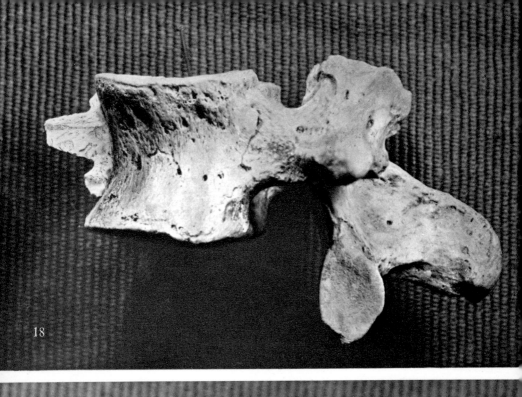

18

19

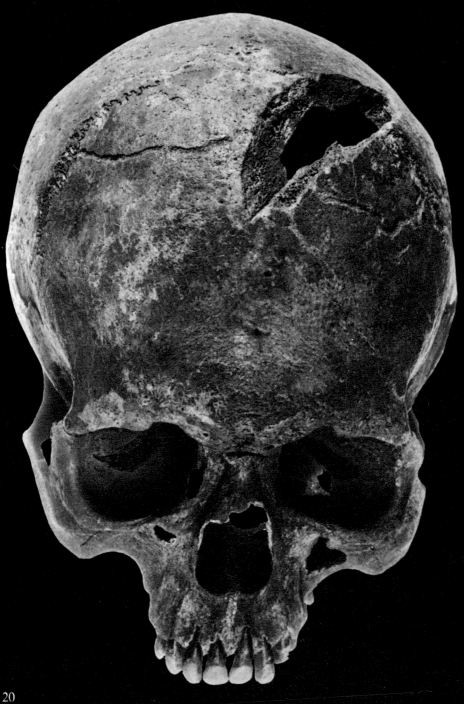

21

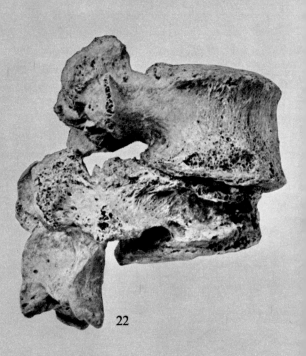

22

23

24

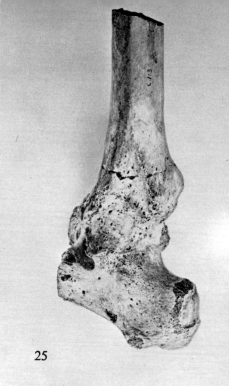

25

26

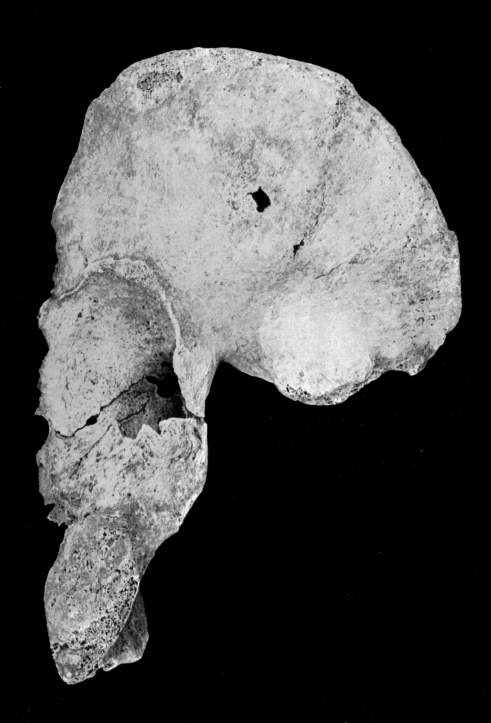

27

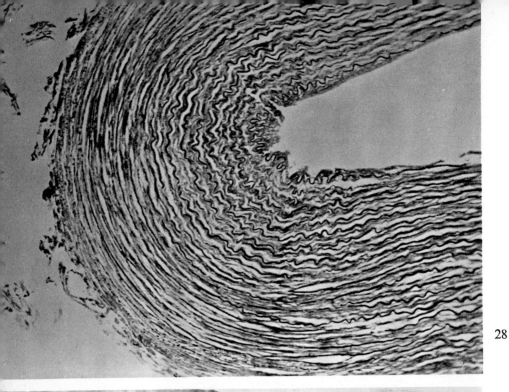

28

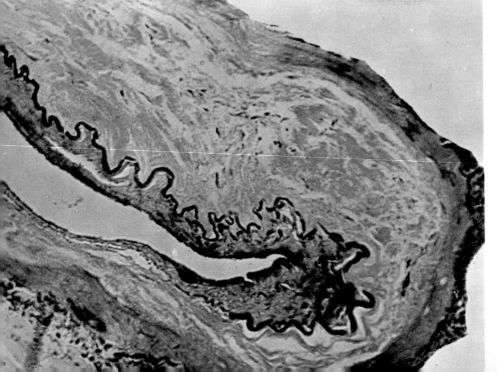

29

32

33

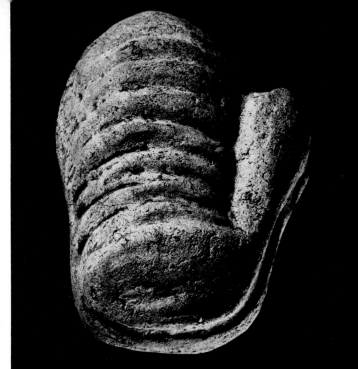

34

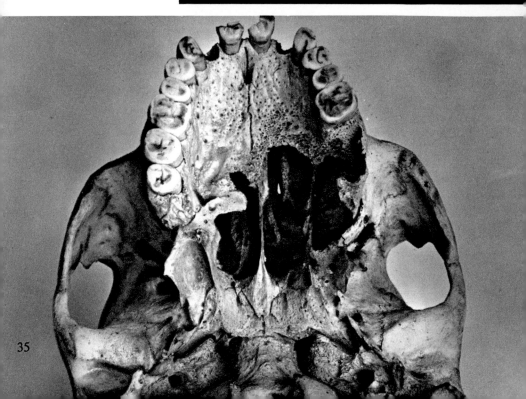

35

36

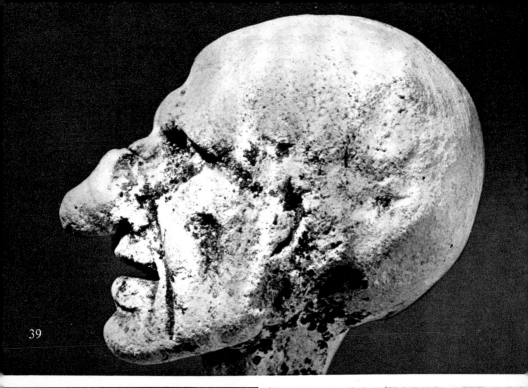

39

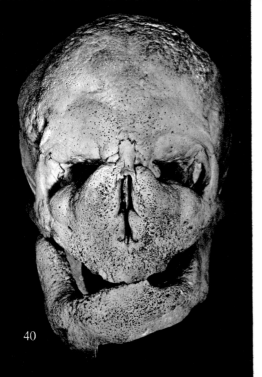

40

41

42

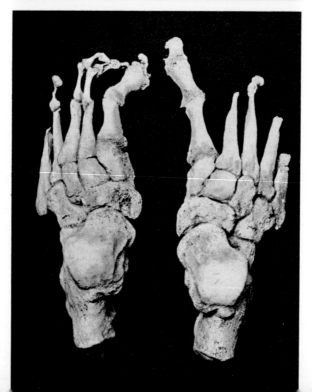

43

45

46

47

48

49

50

51

52

ΘΕΟΙϹ ☥ ΗΡΩϹΙΝ

ΛΟΥΚΙΟϹΜΙΝΙΚΙΟϹΑΝΘΙΜΟϹΚΑΙϹΚΡΕΙ
ΒΩΝΙΑΦΗΛΙΚΙϹϹΙΜΑϹΑΤΥΧΕΙϹΓΟΝΕΙϹ
ΑΜΙΝΙΚΙΩΑΝΘΙΜΩΚΥΝΩΤΕΚΝΩΓΛΥΚΥΤΑΤΩ
ΚΑΙΟΕΩϹΤΕΙΩϹΕΠΗΚΟΩϹΖΗϹΑΝΕΤΗΑΛΛΗΝΑϹΕ
ΝΗΠΙΟϹΕΙΝΤΥΧΩΝΤΥΜΒΟΥΤΟΥΔ.....ΗΝΠΡΟϹΕΠΑ...ΗΝ
ΟϹϹΕΠΑΘΟΝΔΕΝΒΑΙΩΤΩΡΑΝΤΙΛΛΟϹΒΙΟΤΗϹ
ΕΝΚΥΡϹΑϹΑΛΙΠΩϹΕΙΝΩΙΜΩϹϹΕΙϹΙΛΙΟϹΠΑΓΟΝΩΝ
ΚΑΙΜΑΤΗϹΟΥϹϹΑΥΤΟΥΚΑΙΕΙϹΗΝΠΙΑΙΜΑΥΤΟϹϹΘΗΚ.
ΗϹΥΧΟΛΑΘΑΝΑΤΟΚΛΙϹΤΟΥΚΗΜΕΛΛΕΝΕϹΕϹΘΟ...
ΜΟΙΡΑΓΑΡΤΙϹ.ΛΙΝΤΙϹΗΜΟΥΚΕΤΙΚϹ.ΑΝΑΤΙΑΠΛΑ
ΛΥΤΙΚΛΔΗΕΥΡΑΝΟΜΗϹϹΥΕΡΝΙΠΙϹΑΗΙΑϹΠΙΙΟϹ...
ΕΝΑϹΩΡΑΙϹΟΛΙΓΑϹΠΩΝΤΑΡϹ.Λ.ΤΕΤΑΞΕΗΡΗϹΩΝ
ΑΙΩΝΕΝΟϹϹΩΠΗϹΛΟΥΛΑΤΗΛΑΔΥΧΟΥϹΕΝ
ΑΛΛΟΤΑΛΛΗΙ.ΙΩϹΓΕΝΝΗϹΑϹΕΛΑϹΑΤΟΝϹΥΝΟϹΟΝΑΙ.ΗΝ
ΤΟΥΤΟΔΟΚΩΝΟϹΙΛΜΟΙΡΑΝ.ΕΛΗΝϹΙΛΑΥΚϹΙΟϹΕΙ
ΚΑΙΤΟΥϹΑ.ΙΙΑϹΤΕΦΑΝΟϹϹΕΙΛΛϹΚΑΚΙϹΤΗ
ΤΗϹΠΡΟΤΕΡΗϹϹΝΟΥϹϹΩϹΤΩϹΤΥΧΕΙΠΟΤΕΡΗ
ϹΗΥΜΙΝΓΑΡΛΜΟΥΤΕΔΙΟΝΤΠΟΛΟϹϹΕΙΧΕΝΕΓϹΙΟϹΤΟΙϹ
ΕΙΤΕΤΑΜΟΝΜΕΛΙΟΙΤϹΝΕΤΟΥΚΑΙΔΛΟΥΟϹϹΕΑΝΕΙΛΩΝ
ΛΥΓΙΑϹΚΑΙϹΤΟΝΑΧΑϹΤΟΙϹΙϹΚΕΕϹϹΙΝΛΟΝΤΑ
ΚΑΙΤΑΥΘΟϹΑΥΤΟϹϹΕΛΑΘΗΝΙΤΑΜΙΝΟϹϹΤΑΠΑΡΟΙϹϹΕΙ
ΟΥΔΟΥΤΟΙΛΜΟΥΓΕΝΕϹΙϹΛΕΙΝΗΓΙΛΗϹϹΟϹΙϹϹΚΟΡΕϹϹ
ΑΛΛΕΤΕΡΑΝΠΑΛΛΛΟΙΝΟϹΟΝΗΓΑΓϹΙΑϹΤΟϹΛΟΙΡΑ
ϹΤΗΛΑΙΧΝΑΜΟΥΟΙϹΚΩϹΑϹΑΚΑΙϹΚΤΗΞΑϹΤΛΛΟΙΠΑ
ΑΧΡΙϹΟΤΟΥ ΨΥΧΗΝ...ΟΥΛΗΜΗΤΡΟϹΧΕΡϹϹΕΙΛΗΠΤΟϹϹΘΙ
ΤΑΥΤΕΠΑΘΟΝΚΑΙΩΤΕΡΜΑΤΙΝΟΥΒΙΟΤΗϹϹΕΝϹ
ΚΑΙΚΑΤΕΛΕΠΤΟΝΤΗΚΕΔΟΝΑΛΤΥΓΕΡΗΝΤΟΙϹΙΜΕΓΙΝΑ.ΟΙϹ
ΑΙΝΟΜΟΡΟϹΛΕΙΥΑϹΤΡΕΙϹϹΓΥΝΟΜΑΔΑΙΜΟΝΑΛΑϹΤΕΦΑΝΩ.ΤΟΥϹ

53

54

55

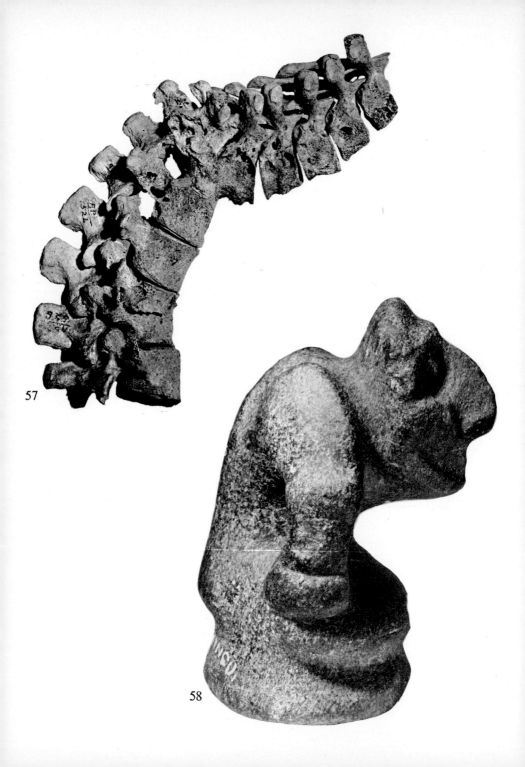

57

58

59

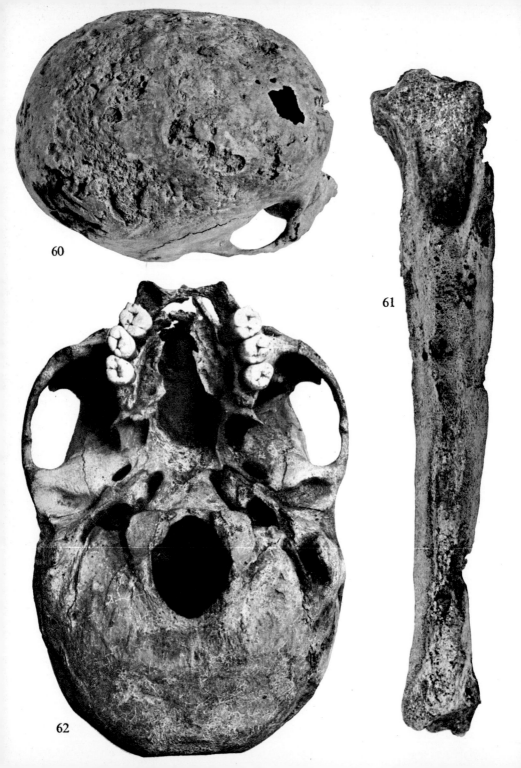

60

61

62

63

64

65

66

67

68

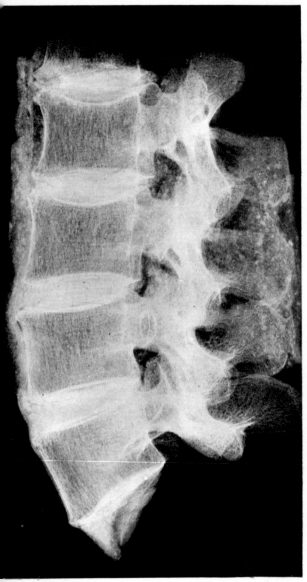

69

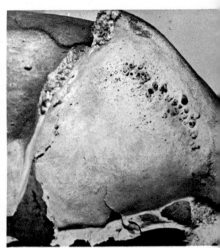

70

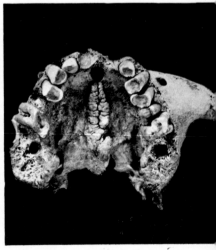

71

72

73

74

75

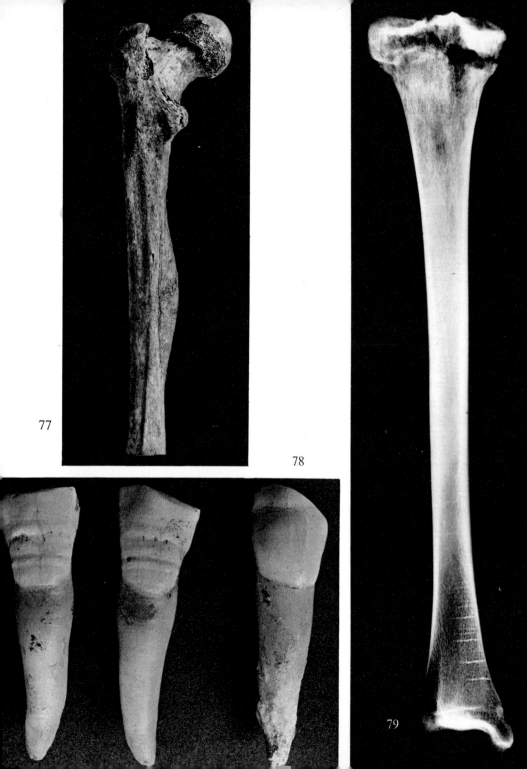

77

78

79

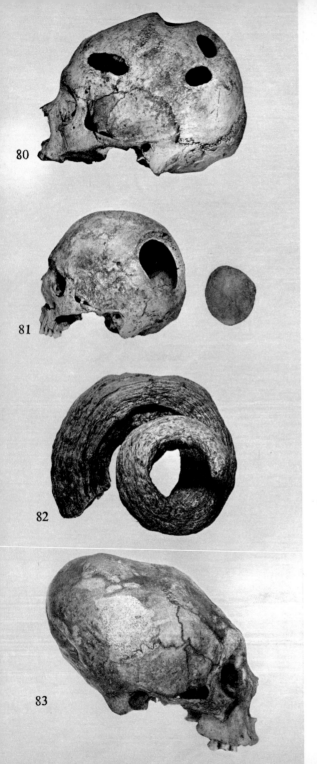

80

81

82

83

84

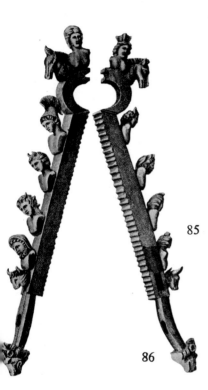

85

86

87

Notes on the Plates

1   The skull of the Rhodesian Man from Broken Hill, Northern Rhodesia. Early Middle Stone Age period. Found in 1921, it is an exaggerated neandertaloid type having features in common with the Florisbad and Saldanha skulls. This lateral view shows the advanced dental and alveolar disease with rotting teeth and paradontal abscesses. The partial destruction of the left mastoid area can be seen. The controversial hole in the temporal bone is visible above the auditory orifice; it is probably due to erosion of the bone from a metastatic abscess. It occurred several days before death and cannot be due to a wound because a posterior branch of the middle meningeal artery runs across it on the interior of the skull; a wound in this position would cause rapidly fatal bleeding. London, British Museum (Natural History) E.686. Photograph British Museum.

2   Lumbar spine of a sixteen-year-old girl. Long Crichel, Dorset. Bronze Age, c. 1600 B.C. The anterior upper margins of the third and fourth vertebrae are defective as a result of an adolescent abnormality of cartilage growth. Author's collection. Photograph Hallam Ashley.

3   A naturally dried mummy. Colombia, South America. Precolumbian. The shrivelled, flexed state of this specimen is typical of Andean mummies and is strongly contrasted with the elaborately embalmed Egyptian type. London, British Museum. Photograph British Museum.

4   Tsantsa or shrunken head. Ecuador, Jívaro tribe. The eyes and lips are sewn up before the shrinking process is begun. This specimen is only 9·6 cm. high. Skin lesions such as ulceration or pustular rashes are occasionally recognizable in these objects. London, British Museum. Photograph British Museum.

5   Wooden puppet figure of a woman. Nigeria, Ibibio. H. 76 cm. Painted yellow with black ornament. Outstretched arms and legs and movable jaw. A protuberant navel is common in African sculpture where it is

usually an artistic convention. But umbilical hernia is extremely common in Bantu Africa and some figures may be intended to show the condition. Non-separation of the umbilical cord after birth is an occasional anomaly which cannot escape notice where people go unclad. In this specimen a hernia and a stump of cord both seem to be present but it may be no more than an artistic fashion—an example of 'pseudo-pathology'. Edinburgh, Royal Scottish Museum 1913.370. Photograph Tom Scott.

6 Limestone bas-relief. Egypt; the tomb of Patenemhab. XVIII Dynasty, *c.* 1350 B.C. This harper is an early portrayal of blindness. The posture of the head and body and the atrophic narrowing of the eyelids break through the stylized canons of Egyptian art to give a convincing picture of a sightless musician. The details of the eye suggest a chronic trachomatous condition. Leyden, Rijksmuseum van Oudheden. Photograph Rijksmuseum.

7 Bronze statuette of a man. Nigeria, Benin. Late sixteenth century. H. 59·5 cm. This is a fine portrayal of achondroplasia. In addition to the typical proportions of the body the artist has caught something of the alert intelligence and vivacious charm that distinguish many, though by no means all, of these dwarfs. The peculiar shape of the head is not characteristic of the disease and is probably due to artificial deformation. Vienna, Museum für Völkerkunde 64.175. Photograph Museum für Völkerkunde.

8 Fresco by Bernardino Luini (1475–1532). This shows St Roch, patron saint of plague victims, pointing to a bubo which the artist has misplaced away from the inguinal lymph glands. Lugano, Chiesa degli Angeli. Photograph Johannes Steiner.

9 The Bayeux tapestry. Probably made in Canterbury, England. *c.* A.D. 1070. Dimensions 50 cm × 70 m. This fragment shows a dwarf groom. France, Bayeux. Photograph J. E. Bulloz.

10 Portrait medallion of Maximianus Herculius (A.D. 284–308). The depressed bridge of the nose suggests a fracture of the nasal bones though

disease, especially syphilis, can give a similar appearance. Paris, Bibliothèque Nationale. Photograph Bibliothèque Nationale.

11 Pottery vessel in the form of a human head scored by incised lines. Step
ornament on the neck. Peru. Chimú culture. H. 15 cm. In spite of
the close resemblance this bears to the condition of double hare-lip it is
more likely to be an artistic convention ultimately derived from a feline
motif. Edinburgh, Royal Scottish Museum 1890.620. Photograph Tom
Scott.

12 Painted limestone bas-relief of the Queen of Punt and attendants.
Egypt, Deir-el-Bahri, from the temple of Hatshepsut. XVIII Dynasty,
c. 1500 B.C. The remarkable figure of the Queen has inspired much
diagnostic ingenuity. The protruding buttocks which, unlike Bushman
steatopygy, are associated with changes of skeletal posture are characteristic of congenital dislocation of the hips. This is a common condition,
especially in females, but there are a few rare diseases that could also
produce this effect and a dogmatic opinion is not justified. Egypt, Cairo
Museum. Photograph Egyptian Service des Antiquités.

13 Painted limestone statue group. Egyptian. VI Dynasty, c. 2500 B.C.
The dwarf Seneb and his family. A brilliant portrayal of achondroplasia
made all the more vivid by the contrast between Seneb and his normal
wife and children. Egypt, Cairo Museum. Photograph Egyptian Service
des Antiquités.

14 Bronze statuette of a man. Nigeria, Benin. Late sixteenth century.
H. 59 cm. Another example of achondroplasia in which the limbs are
even shorter than in most such dwarfs. The head is free from any abnormality. Vienna, Museum für Völkerkunde 64.743. Photograph
Museum für Völkerkunde.

15 Hydrocephaly and microcephaly. The hydrocephalic is from Norton,
Yorkshire. Romano-British. The huge globular head has a capacity of
about 2600 c.c. By contrast the microcephalic from Natal, South Africa,

has a capacity of only 688 c.c. The hydrocephalic is in Cambridge, Duckworth Laboratory Eu. 1.3.6. The microcephalic is in the author's collection. Photograph Hallam Ashley.

16 Calvarium. Egyptian. Roman period. The narrow, keeled appearance of a scaphocephalic skull is well shown in this specimen. The condition is due to premature fusion of the midline sagittal suture. Intellect is unimpaired because compensatory lengthening of the skull is free to occur. Cambridge, Duckworth Laboratory (Unnumbered). Photograph Hallam Ashley.

17 Pottery vase in the form of a human head. Peru, uncertain locality. *c.* thirteenth–fifteenth century A.D. H. 19·5 cm. This *huaco* is an excellent portrait of a mongol, a form of idiocy in which the head is extremely short, the forehead tends to be bulbous, the upper facial height is reduced because the maxilla is small and sunken, with the lower jaw prominent by contrast (mandibular prognathism). Coll. Miss K. Kemper.

18, 19 Human lumbar vertebra. Grotte de la Tourasse, Saint Martory (Haute-Garonne). Neolithic. A flint arrowhead is lodged in the anterior surface of the vertebral body slightly to the left of the midline. To enter the bone at this point the abdominal aorta must have been perforated and death from haemorrhage would have ensued within a few minutes. Toulouse, Muséum d'Histoire Naturelle (unregistered). Photograph Muséum d'Histoire Naturelle.

20 Skull of a middle-aged man. Thorpe St Catherine, Norfolk. Late Saxon period. The position and appearance of the wound is highly typical of an axe or sword cut. The upper part of the wound cuts cleanly through the bone leaving a sharp margin but the force and shock of the blow cause the victim to fall with the weapon deeply embedded in the bone. In falling the cut segment breaks with a jagged edge along the base of the incision. Norwich, Castle Museum 15.953. Photograph Ilford Ltd.

21 Left tibia and fibula. Thetford, Norfolk. Late Saxon period. Both bones have been fractured obliquely and spasm of the muscles has drawn up

the distal fragments until the bones are 2·4 cm. shorter than those of the right leg. Periostitis on the surface of the tibia shows that this was an infected compound fracture but the ultimate repair, though ungainly and independent of surgical endeavour, is sound. Norwich, Castle Museum 167.957/43. Photograph Ministry of Works.

22 Two lumbar vertebrae. Burgh Castle, Suffolk. Early Saxon period. In this specimen fracture of a vertebral body has led to the fusion of two bones. Fractures of this type may follow falls from a height, compression injuries from the collapse of a building on the victim, or may even occur spontaneously from secondary deposits of cancer in the bone. The firm union shown here excludes this last possibility. Norwich, Castle Museum 51.962/47. Photograph Hallam Ashley.

23 Peat bog burial. Grauballe, Denmark. Roman Iron Age, third–fifth century A.D. A man found naked with his throat cut and lying prone in a position familiar from other bog burials. Århus, Forhistorisk Museum. Photograph Forhistorisk Museum.

24 Six thoracic vertebrae. Burgh Castle, Suffolk. Early Saxon period. These bones are fused into a rigid mass (sometimes called 'poker' spine) by the outgrowth of osteophytic lipping. When severe the entire vertebral column may be involved. Norwich, Castle Museum 51.962/117. Photograph Hallam Ashley.

25 Left ankle joint. Caister-on-Sea, Norfolk. Early Saxon. Fusion of bones at a joint (ankylosis) may be due to injury, infection or other causes. In this case it is probably the result of a non-tuberculous infection. Norwich, Castle Museum 343.957/113. Photograph Hallam Ashley.

26 The distal end of a left femur. Burgh Castle, Suffolk. Early Saxon. Jagged outgrowths of osteoarthritis surround the joint and the erosion of cartilage from the end of the bone has resulted in a polished ivory or 'eburnated' appearance due to the grinding of this surface on to the similarly exposed surface of the tibia. Norwich, Castle Museum 51.962/63. Photograph Hallam Ashley.

27 Left hip joint of a middle-aged man. Thetford, Norfolk. Medieval. This is Perthes' disease, a degeneration and erosion of the femoral head with concurrent enlargement and destruction of its socket in the hip bone. Norwich, Castle Museum 471.959/D.IV. Photograph Hallam Ashley.

28 Section across a carotid artery of a male mummy. Stained by Verhoef's method and van Gieson's fluid. Magnification × 160. Early degenerative changes are shown with fibrous tissue appearing between the laminae. Preparation and photograph Dr A. T. Sandison. By courtesy of *Medical History*.

29 Section across an artery from the leg of an elderly female mummy. Stained by Heidenhain's iron-haematoxylin. Reduplication of the internal elastic lamina and fibrosis of the vessel wall are present. These changes are typical of arterio-sclerosis and commonly associated with high blood pressure. Preparation and photograph Dr A. T. Sandison. By courtesy of *Medical History*.

30 Pottery jug. Peru. Mochica period. H. 29 cm. The asymmetrical face is typical of a hemiplegia or stroke. London, British Museum. Photograph British Museum.

31 Wooden dance mask. Liberia, Dan-Ngere peoples. H. 24 cm. The distortion of the face to the left and the flabby protrusion of the right cheek accurately portray what happens to a face that is paralysed on one side. Photograph Eliot Elisofon.

32 Painted wooden mask. Ceylon. H. 23·5 cm. There are many Sinhalese magical practices for curing disease and ex-votos of eyes, limbs, the tongue, testicles and other parts of the body occur as they do in Greece. In Ceylon they are sometimes of silver. The mask shown here with a distorted face was used in the magic ritual for curing lameness. The paradox is explained by the fact that the lameness, like the facial paralysis, would be the result of a cerebral vascular lesion. The cumulative effect

of these facial palsies from different continents suggests that strokes have been widely recognized for many centuries. London, British Museum 1927, 1–8.20. Photograph British Museum.

33 Two caudal vertebrae of a dinosaur, *Apatosaurus louisae* Holland. From the Como beds, Comanchean (Lower Cretaceous) of Wyoming, *c.* 125,000,000 B.P. The nature of the tumour which links these bones is uncertain. On sectioning the mass it is seen to resemble a haemangioma— a tumour formed by excessive proliferation of blood vessels. It could, however, be a kind of exostosis or even simple callus round a fracture. Original in Kansas, University Museum. Photograph (from a cast) Wellcome Historical Medical Museum.

34 Pottery ex-voto. Etruscan. Third century B.C. H. 14·2 cm. This repre-sents an excised uterus. The pear-shaped swelling on the right may be a fibroid tumour or vaginal cyst. Although hysterectomy is described in Greek medical texts we need not suppose that the donor of this ex-voto had herself necessarily undergone the operation. London, British Museum. Photograph British Musem.

35 Adult male skull. Egyptian, III–V Dynasty, *c.* 2700 B.C. Naso-pharyngeal cancer with destruction of the posterior part of the left side of the palate, part of the left upper jaw and the posterior wall of the antrum. An area of osteitis around the primary lesion is due to infection after the growth had ulcerated through the mucous membrane of the nose and mouth. Cambridge, Duckworth Laboratory 236. Photograph Hallam Ashley. By courtesy of *The Journal of Laryngology and Otology.*

36 An ex-voto representing a female torso. Cyprus. The rough surface of the marble below the breasts is clearly the remains of a bunch of grapes, a common fertility symbol. It is most unfortunate that this specimen should have been published as an example of breast cancer or other lesion in a journal with the authority and wide circulation of the *Proceedings of the Royal Society of Medicine of London,* 29: 1015–28. New York, Metropolitan Museum of Art C.S.1434–74.51.2854. Photograph Metropolitan Museum.

37   Statue of a boy. Graeco-Roman. The boy is shown removing a thorn from his foot. With the introduction of agricultural manuring and the domestication of the Equidae the terror of the trivial was always present— a tiny wound might lead to infection by tetanus. Rome, Museo del Capitolino. Photograph Mansell Collection.

38   Painting by Domenico Ghirlandaio (1449–94). The bulbous appearance of the old man's nose is due to rhinophyma, a chronic infection of the skin and underlying tissues which leads to a granulomatous type of thickening. Lesions of this kind seem to be often portrayed in early art. Paris, Musée du Louvre. Photograph J. E. Bulloz 11322.

39   Limestone head. Egyptian. Probably Ptolemaic first century B.C. H. 5·7 cm. Exaggeratedly large noses appear in the art of many countries. Usually they are mere grotesques but several diseases can cause nasal hypertrophy and are likely to attract the eye of an artist. Domenico Ghirlandaio (1449–94) has left a brilliant painting of an old man with a nose made bulbous by rhinophyma (Paris, Louvre). The serious expression on the face of this Egyptian carving suggests that some such chronic inflammatory lesion is intended here rather than a comic caricature. The coins of the Roman emperor Nerva (A.D. 96–98) regularly show him with a long, beaky nose, perhaps from a similar condition. Edinburgh, Royal Scottish Museum 1921.855. Photograph Tom Scott.

40   Skull showing leontiasis ossea. Peruvian. Uncertain provenance and date. The gross thickening of bone, which in extreme cases may almost entirely obliterate the nasal cavity and the eye-sockets, is typical of this disease. It has a multiple pathology, the example shown here being predominantly infective in origin. (A slice of bone has been deliberately removed from the lower border of the mandible.) London, Royal College of Surgeons Museum 1358.I. Gen. Path. Sect. Photograph Royal College of Surgeons.

41   Wooden mask of the Ekpo society. Nigeria, Ibibio tribe. H. 28 cm. The retracted, irregular lips, the nose eroded and broken by disease into blocks of presumably indurated tissue, the deep separation between the

main masses of the facial architecture could be an expression of either leprosy or the gangosa lesions of yaws. Lagos, Nigerian Museum. Photograph K. C. Murray.

42 Steatite Nomali figure. Sierra Leone. Pre-Mende. H. 43 cm. The huge scrotum is probably intended to represent elephantiasis. In this infection the scrotal enlargement may sometimes be so extravagant that the organ reaches to the ground and may measure up to two metres in circumference. The diagnosis here cannot be made with certainty; an alternative would be hydrocoele, a condition in which circum-testicular fluid may accumulate (as in the case of Edward Gibbon) to the extent of two or more gallons. Edinburgh, Royal Scottish Museum 1953.379. Photograph Tom Scott.

43 Feet of an adult female. Naestved, Denmark. Medieval. This is typical of leprosy: the destruction of phalanges, the hourglass appearance of those which remain, the tapering of the metatarsals, the over-all deformity and the signs of chronic inflammation are characteristic of this disease. But to confirm it beyond all doubt cranial changes need to be present also. Roskilde, coll. and photograph of Dr V. Møller-Christensen.

44 Limestone stele. Egyptian, XVIII Dynasty. H. 26·5 cm. This representation of the priest Ruma is the best ancient portrayal of an atrophied limb from paralytic poliomyelitis. Copenhagen, Carlsberg Glyptothek. Photograph Carlsberg Glyptothek.

45 Anthropomorphic pottery vase. Chimbote, Peru. Mochica culture. H. 16 cm. This shows nasal destruction due to *uta*. Scarring and collapse of the tissues of the nose have drawn up the lip which is everted and swollen with fluid. Cambridge, University Museum of Archaeology and Ethnology 47.350. Photograph Museum of Archaeology.

46 Pottery stirrup vase. Peruvian. Mochica period, *c.* A.D. 1–900. H. 21 cm. Red on cream. This is an excellent example of the destruction of the lips and tip of the nose by *uta*. In this case the disease has led to loss of both feet. Coll. Miss K. Kemper.

47 Black-on-white pottery figure containing a whistle. Chancay, Peru. A.D. 1300–1400. H. 24 cm. In normal burials skin diseases vanish without trace; this is an excellent example of a pottery figure recording a dermatological lesion. It probably represents verruga peruana (bartonellosis), a disease, now restricted to the Andean valleys, that is transmitted by a small nocturnal blood-sucking fly, *Phlebotomus verrucorum*. Once again no certainty is possible. The diagnosis rests on a balance of probabilities and the appearance could equally well portray von Recklinghausen's disease, in which the skin is festooned with hundreds of small fibrous tumours. Lima, Museo Nacional de Antropologia y Arqueologia. Photograph Museo Nacional.

48 Turquoise mosaic mask of the god Quetzalcoatl. Aztec, perhaps Mixtec workmanship. Thirteenth–fifteenth century A.D. H. 19 cm. This magnificent object is made with great care from tiny chippings of turquoise. About three dozen larger raised pieces of the stone are scattered over the mask and it is likely that they represent bartonellosis—verruga peruana. It can be seen that the mosaic fragments in the centre of the face, on the cheeks and forehead, are smaller and smoother than the rest; they are also *slightly* darker in colour. (This is not obvious in the plate.) The result is to produce the effect of a feverish, slightly cyanosed flush which does indeed occur in severe cases of the disease. The late Robert Barlow seems to have been the first to suggest that this mask was intended to represent some form of abnormality. It is of great importance historically because it is almost certainly part of the treasure that Montezuma gave to Cortes. London, British Museum. Photograph British Museum.

49 Pottery figurine. Mexico. Maya period. H. 5 cm. In this head the damage to the nose is an artifact but the pits in the tongue are intentional. It is impossible to be certain what disease is intended but they appear to be discharging sinuses, perhaps from a fungal infection such as actinomycosis or a blastomycete. It is just possible that they represent scars from some repeated act of ritual mutilation of the kind shown in Plate 88. London, British Museum. Photograph British Museum.

50 Pottery grain storage jar. Canaanite, from the Amenhotep III temple, Beth-Shan, Jordan. *c.* 1411–1314 B.C. H. 38 cm. The face on this jar is an astonishingly close portrayal of lepromatous leprosy. The thickened skin of the cheeks and forehead is loose and baggy in appearance; the nose is bulbous and deformed; the eyebrows puffy and hairless; the natural creases and folds are exaggerated. All these changes are typical of the disease and innumerable lepers today have a face which closely follows every feature of this jar. Jerusalem, Palestine Archaeological Museum P.1806. Photograph Palestine Archaeological Museum.

51 Wooden figurine of a man. Egyptian. Predynastic. H. 10 cm. This is probably the oldest surviving work of art to show tuberculosis of the spine (Pott's disease). The hunchbacked curvature and slight lateral deviation of the vertebral column are present in innumerable cases of this disease. But all such specimens remain ambiguous: the appearance of this figure *could* be due to other infections or to a fracture. Tuberculosis is, however, the likeliest single cause of this deformity and the cumulative evidence of many such statuettes from different cultures is impressive. Bruxelles, Musée de la Cinquantenaire. Photograph Musée de la Cinquantenaire.

52 Ivory figurine of a negro. Greek, possibly from Italy. First century A.D. H. 10·5 cm. This depicts a negro slave with Pott's disease. There is a well-marked hunchback deformity (not seen in this view) with an asymmetrical 'pigeon' chest. The curvature of the spine makes the head sink between the shoulders. The weariness of the facial expression and a suggestion of difficulty in breathing, both brilliantly portrayed, are typical of this disease. London, British Museum Towneley Collection 1959, 4–15.2. Photograph British Museum.

53 Greek sepulchral inscription. Smyrna. *c.* 100 B.C.–A.D. 100. The cause of death is often given in classical funeral stelae but this specimen is unique in recording extensive clinical details of a case of generalized tuberculosis. The inscription proper consists of twenty-seven lines of dactylic hexameters. C.I.G. 3272; *Epigrammata Graeca*, ed. Kaibel, 314. Rome, Palazzo Barberini. Photograph German Archaeological Institute at Rome.

54 Painted pottery tomb figure. Chinese. Third–second century B.C. H. 21·5 cm. The back view of this figure shows the curvature and lateral deflection of the spine, with the head seemingly sunk between the shoulders, that is typical of vertebral tuberculosis. Kansas City, Coll. and photograph Laurence Sickman.

55 Anterior view of the same figure. Although it is partly conceived in the form of a grotesque it seems to be based on a realistic portrayal of Pott's disease.

56 Wooden figurine, probably a stopper for a gourd flask. Ghana, Ashanti. H. 20·5 cm. The posture of this figure with a gibbous curvature of the spine, forward bowing of the shoulders, slightly flexed legs and the hands supporting some of the weight of the body by counter-thrusting against the top of the thighs is again characteristic of tuberculous collapse of the vertebrae. So, too, is the anxious 'pinched' expression on the face. The total effect of these figurines from many parts of the world leaves little doubt that they are intended to portray Pott's disease. London, British Museum, Mrs Gordon Barclay collection W.298. Photograph British Museum.

57 Thoraco-lumbar region of adult female spine. Avon, Livingston County, New York State. Seneca Indian. Thirteenth–fifteenth century A.D. Seven thoracic and five lumbar vertebrae are involved in a disease process which has led to the almost total destruction of one vertebral body, the collapse of others and their fusion in a sharply angled position. The many drainage channels that can be seen indicate the extent to which the bones were filled and surrounded with pus. These changes are far more likely to be due to tuberculosis than to any other condition and the specimen is therefore a crucial one for the establishment of Pott's disease in pre-columbian America. It is not conclusive, however: this appearance *could* be the result of an actinomycotic fungal infection or a staphylococcal osteomyelitis. Rochester (N.Y.), Museum of Arts and Sciences AP 526. Photograph Rochester Museum of Arts and Sciences.

58 Stone grain-pounder, probably representing a maize god. San Domingo. Precolumbian. H. 15 cm. Yet another specimen with the typical hunched

back of spinal tuberculosis. In cases such as this where the pigeon-
chested deformity is absent or unobtrusive the head is often thrown far
forward instead of being drawn down between the shoulders. London,
British Museum. Photograph British Museum.

59 Pottery vase. Chancay, Peru. Thirteenth–fifteenth century A.D. H. 17·5
cm. Black and brown on white. This beautiful *huaco* shows the typical
features of Pott's disease: severe angulation of the spine, pigeon chest,
slight lateral curvature with rotation of the spine and ribs, and the head
apparently sunken between high-pitched shoulders. Skinny limbs,
though commonly found in vertebral tuberculosis, are only an artistic
convention in this vase. London, Coll. Miss K. Kemper.

60 Adult female skull. Spitalfields, London. Before 1537. The rough
appearance of this skull with 'snail track' ulcers eroding the bone and
thickened areas of osteitis around and between the ulcers is typical of
syphilis. This specimen is among the earliest to be recognized as a definite
example of the disease. The graveyard of St Mary Spittle was closed in
1537 and this skull cannot be later than that date. Cambridge, Duckworth Laboratory SF.131. Photograph Hallam Ashley.

61 The cavity of a right tibia showing advanced syphilis. A specimen
prepared by John Hunter (1728–93). The combination of necrotic
areas interspersed with osteophytic thickening and fistulous openings
extending into the marrow cavity is characteristic of this stage of the
disease. London, Hunterian Museum, Royal College of Surgeons P.745.
Photograph Royal College of Surgeons.

62 Adult male skull. Australian aborigine, Victoria. Pre-white. All teeth
anterior to the molars have been lost as a result of a necrosis of the bony
alveolus. The hard palate has also been destroyed by ulceration which has
extended through to the nasal cavity. From the appearance of this skull it
would be almost impossible to exclude leprosy, so closely does it resemble
that disease. In fact, the survival of other parts of the skeleton proves that
this is yaws (framboesia) and the facial lesions are those of its 'gangosa'
manifestation. London, Wellcome Medical Museum 54 (94.5)/31.
Photograph C. J. Hackett.

63 Pottery vase. Peru. Mochica period. H. 28 cm. In this striking portrait head the taut lines of nose and cheek and eyebrows, together with the tight-drawn mouth, reveal the tenseness of the underlying muscles. The neck is full, though not abnormally so, but the dominant feature is the protruding eyes with a wide band of 'white' (conjunctiva) between the upper lid and the pupil. This complex of physical signs is characteristic of toxic goitre—an abnormally active thyroid gland—and it may be that the pot was modelled on just such a case. But again the diagnosis must be considered as no more than tentative: no example of the disease has yet been identified in a mummy and there is little chance that it will be. London, British Museum. Photograph British Museum.

64 Terracotta female figurine. Greek: Boeotia. Fourth century B.C. H. 19·2 cm. This statuette, which may represent an elderly hetaira, is perhaps only meant to portray a common tendency to obesity. But it suggests an endocrine disorder and could be an admirable representation of Cushing's disease. London, British Museum C.243. Photograph British Museum.

65 Painted pottery jug. Chicama valley, Peru. Mochica period. H. 26·2 cm. The podgy face and thick dumpy body of this figure suggest that it may represent an endocrine disease of the 'Fat Boy of Peckham' type. Cambridge, University Museum of Archaeology and Ethnology 24.189. Photograph Museum of Archaeology and Ethnology.

66 Pottery head of a man. Nigeria. Nok culture, c. first century B.C. H. 16 cm. This curious figure is difficult to interpret. The two lumps on the head might be intended to represent sebaceous cysts of the scalp but there is also an irregularity round the mouth, with a defective upper lip and erosion or blocking of the left nostril. This whole complex of lesions could be due to yaws or perhaps even a malignant growth of the naso-oral region with secondary deposits in the vault of the skull. Nigeria, Jos Museum. Photograph Jos Museum.

67 Wooden figure of a woman. New Guinea, Lower Sepik River. H. 24·5 cm. Large swellings are shown over the joints in this figure. In the plate they are especially clear on the left knee and ankle and the right elbow.

They may be nothing more than a part of the artist's technique for depicting a joint but juxta-articular swellings of precisely this kind are found in endemic syphilis and other diseases and it is likely that a pathological condition inspired the carving of this figurine. London, British Museum. Photograph British Museum.

68 Limestone portrait head of Akhenaten (Amenhotep IV). Egypt. XVIII Dynasty, *c.* 1365 B.C. The exceptional length of the lower jaw is highly characteristic of acromegaly. The nose and upper jaw are slightly but not conspicuously enlarged in this portrait. There is almost certainly an element of pituitary dysfunction underlying this degree of mandibular hypertrophy. Berlin, Ägyptisches Museum 14512. Photograph Staatliche Museen zu Berlin.

69 Lateral radiograph of the lumbar spine of a female mummy. Egyptian. XXVI Dynasty, seventh century B.C. The dense, white, radio-opaque bands of the intervertebral discs are due to alkaptonuric ochronosis. In a normal radiograph the bodies of the vertebrae are moderately opaque, as here, but the discs, being radiolucent, do not appear on the film and the intervertebral spaces seem to be empty. This radiograph was taken after removal of the spine from the body. It is fully described in Wells and Maxwell (1962), *Brit. J. Radiol.*, 35:679–82. Norwich, Castle Museum 242.27. Radiograph Dr B. M. Maxwell. By courtesy of *The British Journal of Radiology.*

70 Skull showing cribra orbitalia. Thetford, Norfolk. Late Saxon period. The bones of the face are missing and a clear view of the roof of the eye-socket can be obtained. The pitting is typical of cribra (or 'usura' as Møller-Christensen prefers to call it). Its cause is uncertain and probably not constant. It is especially frequent in skulls of ancient Egyptian children. Norwich, Castle Museum 167.957/31. Photograph Hallam Ashley.

71 Upper jaw of adult male. Caister-on-Sea, Norfolk. Early Saxon. The teeth are heavily worn and chipped from rough usage. Several have been shed during life. The pitting, roughness and distortion of the bony gums (alveolus) reveal that this man suffered from a severe infection of his jaw.

This is typical of the gingivitis, pyorrhoea and underlying osteitis that is found in severe cases of scurvy. The thick raised ridge down the middle of the palate is a torus—a congenital anomaly unconnected with disease. Norwich, Castle Museum 343.957/B. Photograph Hallam Ashley.

72 Limestone terminal of a drip-mould. Clarendon Palace, Wiltshire. *c.* A.D. 1240. H. 21·5 cm. It has been thought that this fine example of Gothic portraiture is intended to represent Death; but the eyes, puckered into mere slits, the wrinkled questioning forehead, the pose of the head and the slightly parted lips are even more characteristic of blindness. Salisbury, South Wilts and Blackmore Museum 80/56. Photograph South Wilts and Blackmore Museum.

73 Wooden mask. Nigeria, Ohafia, Ibo tribe. H. 29 cm. This represents a one-eyed man who cannot find his mouth to use his chewing-stick to clean his teeth. It is used in a mime associated with the New Yam Festival. Lagos, Nigerian Museum. Photograph K. C. Murray.

74 Bronze statue of Karaikkal-Ammaiyar, a saint of Siva. Indian. Twelfth-fourteenth century A.D. H. 41·2 cm. The thin, wasted limbs, prominent ribs, scraggy neck and general emaciation point to chronic malnutrition. The relative fullness of the face is partly due to the conventional portrayal of the character. Kansas City, William Rockhill Nelson Gallery of Art. Photograph William Rockhill Nelson Gallery.

75 Back view of the same figure.

76 A right tibia (sectioned), left tibia and fibula (uncut). Alice Springs, Australia. Female aborigine. This is 'boomerang leg', a condition traditionally thought to be due to yaws. Recent work has cast some doubt on this aetiology. London, Wellcome Medical Museum. Photograph C. J. Hackett.

77 Left femur of adult male. Caister-on-Sea, Norfolk. Early Saxon. The long, low swelling on the medial (right) side of the shaft is the result of a blood clot that has ossified. Haemorrhage, clotting and eventual bone formation of this kind commonly occur under the periosteal membrane in

cases of scurvy. That this man suffered from the disease is shown by the state of his upper jaw (Plate 71). Norwich, Castle Museum 343.957/B. Photograph Hallam Ashley.

78 A pair of adult incisor teeth. Thetford, Norfolk. Saxon. A single adult canine. Congham, Norfolk. Medieval. The ridge and furrow appearance of these teeth is due to defects of nutrition or to other adverse influences during their developing period. It is one form of enamel hypoplasia. The unpaired tooth has a root roughened by peridontal infection; a small abscess cavity surrounded it in the jaw. Norwich, Castle Museum 167.957/44 and 90.955/3. Photograph Hallam Ashley.

79 Radiograph of a right tibia. Caister-on-Sea, Norfolk. The white transverse lines (Harris's lines) at the distal end were produced by phases of arrested growth due to illness or starvation. At least nine such episodes can be identified. The lines nearest the middle of the bone precede those nearer the ankle joint. The absence of lines from the proximal end of the shaft is due to intrusive silt which entered through the defect in the head of the bone and masks their presence. Norwich, Castle Museum 343.957/61. Radiograph Ilford Ltd.

80 Trephined male skull. Cuzco, Peru. *c.* A.D. 1000. This remarkable specimen has seven well-healed elliptical trephine openings of which four can be seen in this plate. The smooth margins of the holes prove that the patient survived all the operations. Multiple trepanning is not exclusive to America: four healed openings are present in a Bronze Age skull from Jericho (2000 B.C.). London, British Museum (Natural History) 1956.10.10.1. Photograph British Museum.

81 Trephined male skull. Crichel Down, Dorset. Beaker period, *c.* 1800 B.C. Size of opening 7·4 × 6·6 cm. This large trephination shows no sign of healing. The rondelle has been removed by cutting round it with a sharp instrument. This skull is rare in having had the rondelle replaced in position when it was buried. Cambridge, Duckworth Laboratory Eu.1.4.57. Photograph Hallam Ashley.

82 A sebaceous horn removed by the author from the head of a woman aged seventy-four. These 'horns' are formed from sebaceous cysts that have burst and discharged their contents. The exposed layer of sebum dries, hardens and is gradually elongated by continued secretion from within the cyst. This specimen measures 38 cm. round the outer border of the spiral. It is included here as an example of the many lesions that may mimic a trephination. It had been slowly growing for forty-five years; when it was removed the underlying parietal bone was found to have an almost circular hole in it about 2·5 cm. in diameter, with gently bevelled sides, a healed margin with no visible diploë, and a roughened area of mild periostitis around it. It was, in effect, indistinguishable from a well-healed trephination. Unfortunately the circumstances of its removal at a small suburban hospital did not permit a photographic record to be obtained. Author's collection.

83 Artificially deformed skull. Vancouver Island, British Columbia, probably Kwakiutl tribe. This type of oblique fronto-occipital compression can be produced by strapping a child's head into an apparatus such as that shown in Figure 33. Many people today are incredulous that distortions of this severity could ever have been considered beautiful. This is a sterile and unrewarding attitude. Whatever, in any age or place, has been esteemed as beauty should still be considered beautiful and it is the enriching task of the scientific aesthete to find out why. Cambridge University, Department of Anatomy. Photograph Department of Anatomy.

84 Pottery bottle. Cayalti, Peru. Chimú culture. H. 30·4 cm. Human head wearing a knitted cap. The bulge in the right cheek is not a sebaceous cyst or any other kind of tumour; it is meant to show that a quid of coca is being chewed. Edinburgh, Royal Scottish Museum 1909.243. Photograph Tom Scott.

85 Mosaic. Byzantine Greek. Eleventh century A.D. The tense lineaments of the face and the apprehensively alert eyes of this mosaic of the Pantokrator appear to reflect a personality in which anxiety neurosis was a prominent trait. Greece, Church of Daphni. Photograph Spyros Meletzis, Athens.

86 Bronze clamp, probably used for ritual castration in the rites of Cybele. River Thames, London Bridge. Romano-British, second–third century A.D. H. 28·7 cm. Originally hinged and closed by a screw nut, it has been broken, perhaps intentionally by an early Christian iconoclast, and repaired. The ornaments on the sides are from top to bottom: Left— Cybele, Stallion, Ares, Artemis, Helios, Chronos, Bull and Lion; Right—Attis, Stallion, Ceres, Aphrodite, Zeus, Hermes, Bull and Lion. It shows evidence of hard and prolonged use. London, British Museum 56.7—1.33. Photograph British Museum.

87 Pottery figure representing a sun god. Nebaj, Mexico. Maya. H. 27 cm. The upper central incisor teeth are shown as having had a piece chipped or filed from the lateral corner of the biting edge. London, British Museum. Photograph British Museum.

88 Carved stone lintel. Menché, Chiapas, Mexico. Maya, *c.* A.D. 780. A kneeling man draws a cord threaded with aloe thorns through his tongue as a blood offering whilst a priest stands over him. Both figures have artificially deformed heads. London, British Museum. Photograph British Museum.